PE

SMALL ACTS OF FREEDOM

Gurmehar Kaur is an Indian student activist and the ambassador for Postcards for Peace, a charitable organization that works towards eliminating discrimination. She is also the co-founder of Citizens for Public Leadership, an independent and non-partisan movement focused on advocating progressive public policy in India. In October 2017, she was listed by *TIME* magazine as a global 'Next Generation Leader'. *Small Acts of Freedom* is her first book.

small acts of freedom

GURMEHAR KAUR

PENGUIN BOOKS
An imprint of Penguin Random House

PENGUIN BOOKS

USA | Canada | UK | Ireland | Australia
New Zealand | India | South Africa | China

Penguin Books is part of the Penguin Random House group of companies
whose addresses can be found at global.penguinrandomhouse.com

Published by Penguin Random House India Pvt. Ltd
7th Floor, Infinity Tower C, DLF Cyber City,
Gurgaon 122 002, Haryana, India

First published in Penguin Books by Penguin Random House India 2018

10 9 8 7 6 5 4 3 2 1

ISBN 9780143442318

Typeset in Garamond Premier Pro by Manipal Digital Systems, Manipal
Printed at Thomson Press India Ltd, New Delhi

www.penguin.co.in

To the memory of my father,
and to my mother for keeping his memories alive

small acts of freedom

Introduction

In February 2017, a few friends asked me if I wanted to join them for a protest at Ramjas College. I said no. I did not know the details of the protest. I wish I had known then what I know now—that they were protesting against campus violence, that all they wanted was the right to conduct a seminar on 'Cultures of Protest'. Little did I know how important peace activism and protest culture would turn out to be for me in the months to come. At the time, as a student of Lady Shri Ram College, I had only heard bits and pieces here and there, read a few social media updates and seen a few articles. I had attended a few events in the past within the Delhi University activism circuit, so it didn't come as a surprise that they expected me to go. I had been very vocal in college, always striking up political conversations and debate, but that day I had a lot on my mind.

Earlier in February, I had had a falling-out with a few friends I deeply cared about and loved. I was still nursing the wounds and dealing with the emotional drama that came along with it. All of this was during the final month of the semester, when we were supposed to submit our assignments. I was studying English and I loved my course, so I buried myself under reading assignments and worked to avoid thinking about my personal dilemmas. Why am I telling you about my personal dilemmas and my arguments with friends? It's because I want you to know that I was living an *ordinary* life, a teenager's life. My head was full of gossip and clothes and trends and books and other things you might expect me to be occupied with. I don't feel like that girl any more. Today, I think about censorship and freedom of expression; I think about liberalism and online abuse; I think about the state of our nation far more frequently than I ever did in those days.

With my exams coming, the Ramjas College fest was the last thing on my mind. In fact, after a rough time at our own fest that year, I wanted to run away as far as I could from the very word itself. I had my own problems. Ramjas can sort out its freedom of expression issue on its own, I thought, and left to get a coffee. My best friend joined me and we sat to do our work. Every so often, we'd chatter about college gossip—who was doing what, who was standing for what post on the students' union, whom we should vote for and if the previous union was corrupt or not. Our phones were on airplane mode because both of us knew that there was no way we could manage to finish our work if there were Instagram and Facebook notifications begging us to glance at our phones.

That evening, when we got back to our rooms and turned off the airplane mode, our phones started buzzing with WhatsApp messages. What was going on? Why was everyone panicking? My phone was flooded with harrowing pictures of violence. These were not pictures that were being circulated by the media—who tended to blow things out of proportion anyway—but those that were being sent to us, in real time, by our own friends who were there.

It all happened in a blur. The students—who had been peacefully protesting to condemn campus violence involving the Akhil Bharatiya Vidyarthi Parishad (ABVP)—were roughed up. There were long messages telling us what had happened and asking if any of us could shelter the injured girls. But as is the case with most college hostels, no one could enter ours after a certain hour. I was told that students were lathi-charged at the protest and shoved into police vans. Then they were taken to a metro station and left there.[1]

A series of emotions ran through me. I felt anger, closely followed by helplessness. What could I have done, sitting in my hostel with a curfew of 8.30 p.m.? How could I help when I could not even go out, I kept wondering. This wasn't just breaking news on TV, these were injustices happening to my own friends. It is so easy to dismiss the bad in the world when it is playing on your TV screens like a movie. You start to think it's all fiction but it never is. It is happening somewhere in the world, to real people, and this time it was happening to people

---

[1] *Business Standard*, 'Ramjas College Scuffle: Delhi Police Suspends Three Cops after Lathicharge', 24 February 2017, http://bit.ly/2B2lt2s.

I knew, people I saw in my college every day, laughing and smiling.

How does one resist?

I took a piece of paper—one side of which, in fact, had notes from the previous semester—and two different coloured pens. Red and black. My friend wrote down the message we had just sat together and framed. I stood with my back to the white wooden door, holding up the sheet as my friend clicked a picture. It was uploaded with a caption on my Facebook profile page.

This is what the placard said: 'I am a student from Delhi University. I am not afraid of ABVP. I am not alone. Every student of India is with me. #StudentsAgainstABVP.'

So what really happened at Ramjas? The truth is, after that picture was uploaded, no one cared to find out.

All of a sudden, I became the focus of a conversation I had not even started. No one could have predicted the events that followed. I became coloured by the narratives people imposed on me: I was the girl with the placard, but I was also the anti-national, the martyr's daughter, the student activist.

It was an easier conversation to have than the one that was actually at hand. It was comfortable to overlook the tamaṣha of rape, death threats and nationalism and focus on a college girl and her Facebook profile picture instead. They—the people who suddenly became furious with me—didn't care about what the placard said, they cared about who held it. Students from one of the top colleges in India were pelted with stones, hurt, manhandled; women were groped, teased and sent anonymous threats; but I understand why the nation wasn't having this conversation. It was too difficult. We would rather shut our eyes than be witnesses to this violence—it helps us sleep in peace.

I'm not someone who always speaks up about everything. I'm guilty of it too and I sleep in peace. Even as I write this, there is so much going on in the world that I haven't spoken about. It seems futile sometimes, just talking, just saying something. But that day, after hearing about my friends being manhandled, silence did not seem like an option. I could not have walked into my college and looked my friends in the eye. I knew I wouldn't be able to. I had lucked out when I said no to them that afternoon, I had escaped the violence, and now guilt was creeping up on me.

What happened at Ramjas College? My friend, who was present there, told me her story. She doesn't want to be named, and understandably so. Who would want to go through what I had for the mere act of speaking up?

On 21 February 2017, a literary event organized by the English department and the literary society of Ramjas College was disrupted by members of the ABVP.[2] It was meant to be a series of panel discussions on 'Cultures of Protest', featuring speakers such as Umar Khalid and Shehla Rashid of Jawaharlal Nehru University and other prominent speakers like Sanjay Kak and Dilip Simeon.[3] According to my friend, all the society members had reached the Ramjas campus by nine that morning. After setting up the registration desk and putting up the posters, they went to the conference hall to attend the first panel discussion. After the first panel, around 11.30 a.m., they heard from

---

[2] Akshit Sangomla, 'ABVP Disrupts, Vandalizes Literary Event at Ramjas College', The Wire, 22 February 2017, http://bit.ly/2AZEB1p.

[3] Livemint, 'DU Autonomous, Won't Intervene in Ramjas College Issue: Prakash Javadekar', 23 February 2017, http://bit.ly/2zG1rO6.

someone that a mob was outside the main gate. Almost one hour before Umar Khalid's talk, the society members were notified that the principal had cancelled his invitation and a few professors were already in his office. This was odd since they had already been told that the principal was okay with Khalid coming to the college for the festival. The itinerary had been out for four or five days. There had been no prior objections. Khalid was meant to speak about the Adivasis in Bastar, and several students from various colleges had come for this discussion. When the society members spoke to the college president and the ABVP intellectual cell head, they were told that as the police wouldn't be able to offer security on campus, Umar Khalid's and Shehla Rashid's invitations had been cancelled.[4]

As soon as the announcement was made, some of the visitors on the campus started hooting and sloganeering, 'Bharat Mata Ki Jai!'[5] By the time

---

[4] Heena Kausar, 'Delhi's Ramjas College Cancels Invite to JNU Students Umar Khalid, Shehla Rashid', *Hindustan Times*, 8 March 2017, http://bit.ly/2AHYFol.

[5] Sangomla, 'ABVP Disrupts, Vandalizes Literary Event'.

all this commotion was over, the second panel discussion had ended. The organizers went to the conference room. They addressed the crowd and explained why the invitations of the two JNU students were cancelled. Those attending the seminar decided to do a protest walk against the ABVP, the students' union members and the Delhi Police. Over a hundred people started walking from the conference hall to the principal's office, to the library lawns and back to the conference hall. When they reached the canteen, they were confronted by a mob who began to abuse them and push them aggressively. The Delhi Police had created a wall between the disruptors and the students.[6]

The police were successful in taking a few people inside the conference room, but had locked them inside. The others couldn't go inside because the conference room was locked and they couldn't go downstairs because the ABVP supporters had become very violent.[7] Everyone was scared. The students locked inside had to

[6] Sangomla, 'ABVP Disrupts, Vandalizes Literary Event'.

[7] Jaideep Deo Bhanj, 'Clashes at Ramjas College in Delhi over Cancellation of Invite to Umar Khalid', *The Hindu*, 22 February 2017, http://bit.ly/2zH2mgX.

break open the lock so that those who were left behind could enter.

Once everyone was inside, they decided to resume their third panel discussion without Umar Khalid. The mob and their supporters downstairs started playing music and dancing at the amphitheatre. The organizers closed all the windows and continued the seminar.

According to S. Santhoshkumar Singh, a student of Ramjas College:

> They were determined to hurt us in every possible way. They attacked us, even girls and professors, as if we were their enemies in a critical battlefield. I saw one of them charging towards us, with a half-cut log in hand, committed to hit anyone standing against them. They tore shirts and dragged and whacked anyone within their reach.

But then, a glass window shattered.[8] The mob started pelting stones at the students.[9]

---

8 Kausar, 'Delhi's Ramjas College Cancels Invite'.

9 Ibid.

In another five minutes, the electricity went out and they were trapped in the conference room for thirty to forty minutes. The students were told by their professors to evacuate the conference room as the police had advised them to do so, keeping their safety in mind. It wasn't safe to stay in the conference hall any more. They were escorted by the police to the back gate of the college.

The following day, a march was organized by the All India Students' Association (AISA) in solidarity with the Ramjas College students. A mob blocked the main gate. The students of the college weren't allowed to leave their own campus.[10] The mob surrounded them, with only a human chain of police separating them from the mob. They were all so scared that someone suggested that the girls take off their earrings, just in case they were attacked.[11]

---

[10] Bhanj, 'Clashes at Ramjas College in Delhi'.

[11] Heena Kausar, 'Ramjas College Protest Highlights: Clashes between ABVP, DU Students, Cops Crack Down,' *Hindustan Times*, 6 March 2017, http://bit.ly/2AGXNjZ.

The students decided to sit down and sing songs of love and friendship instead. Aman Bhardwaj, a student who was present, said:

> Even when we encountered violence and police apathy, we did not respond with violence. This was in part due to our fear of backlash and a further round of violence which could potentially spiral into a riot, and partly due to our own non-violent ethos. Instead we sang songs using our creativity and imagination. For example, slogans like '*Desh ke gaddaron ko, joote maaro saalon ko*' were countered by songs meant to caricature their seriousness, like '*Tareef karun kya uski, jisne tumhe banaya*'.

Around 1.20 p.m., the police escorted them towards the back gate. At this point, the crowd managed to push through the police protection and viciously attack the students.[12]

While some of the students were trying to speak to the policemen in the front, the attacks

[12] Kausar, 'Ramjas College Protest Highlights'.

continued from the sides and the back.[13] One of my friends said, 'Students were crying. I don't remember feeling so unsafe and threatened in my life.'

Some of the girls stood up and made a human wall around the students to protect them from the mob. Another student was threatened because she was taking a video of the mob misbehaving with the professors. Around 4.30 p.m., the police escorted the students to the police buses and dropped them off at the Civil Lines metro station. My friend and other protesters received several threats later in the evening, stating they were going to be witch-hunted. They all had to leave the campus and stay with friends for a few days.

This was the information I had. This was what was told to me. This was what was not being talked about on prime-time TV shows. Those shows

[13] The Wire, 'Students, Faculty Protesting ABVP Violence Attacked by Thugs inside Ramjas College', 22 February 2017, http://bit.ly/2CEdt8D.

spoke about ideologies and nationalism and everything other than the injured students. These were eighteen-year-old first-year undergraduate students who had come to college for an education, to find themselves and their ideologies. All their lives they had studied hard to get here. Who knows how many battles they had fought? Some had economic problems, some had to fight their families to be in Delhi. Everyone who had come to that college had waged their own tiny battles and this is what happened to them. How is it correct? How can we justify this in the name of nationalism, or hell, in the name of anything? What is nationalism? Beating eighteen-year-old students of a top college to pulp because they didn't adhere to the ideology you wanted to impose on them?

Later, I asked Shehla Rashid about this incident and she wrote to me: 'The takeaway from the incident is that we should not be afraid of these cowardly tactics, and stand together instead. This is the model of resistance that we need to replicate across the country in order to save India from the fascist regime.'

I have often wondered ever since if I could go back and do it all over again. Knowing the consequences, would I? And every time, in about a heartbeat, I say yes. All my life I wanted to be strong and just like my father, I wanted to serve the country—the people of the country—and what I did was a part of that. It was my duty as a citizen, as a student and as a friend to resist.

∽

But here's what happened. After my picture with the placard went viral on social media, all sorts of things were dug out. A year previously, as part of a peace campaign I had participated in, I appeared in a video in which I held up a placard which read, 'Pakistan did not kill my father, war killed him.'

Does this seem callous? I genuinely believe that war is cruel and pointless and unnecessary. I lost my father to war. If anyone knows the damage war can do, it's the family of an officer.

That video—which no one had paid attention to at the time—now resurfaced on social media. Screenshots of me were suddenly being shared online as further proof of my 'anti-national' tendencies. I had never faced as much hate as I did in the three days that followed. I had never even known that this much hate was possible.

People I revered and respected—celebrities, politicians, the media—went after me with a kind of vitriol that I could barely comprehend at first. From strangers, I received abuse and threats. It seemed that everyone had an opinion on my political beliefs but no one actually wanted to ask me what these were.

What bothered me the most was the unspoken accusation that I was *not* patriotic. At first, I couldn't articulate clearly why this bothered me so much. With hindsight, I now know what it was. The idea that I—a girl who had lost her father in the cause of the nation—didn't *care* about this country was not just ridiculous or laughable, it was actually hurtful. My father taught me more about the real meaning of patriotism in the few years I knew him than anyone else in the years that followed. He was brilliant, brave and loving, and he taught me that a love of peace was more patriotic than any macho enthusiasm for the battlefield. He taught me that hatred does not solve any problem in the world. And he taught me to stand up for myself.

I want no one to go through what I went through, what my family went through. I've had to live without a father for more years than I've lived with one. Why would I want anyone else to experience that? And all the people who expressed their hatred and accused me of apathy—they will never know how much I've had to struggle to get over the loss of my father.

I've been trolled, mocked and bullied. I've had people call me names. And I've been frightened for my life. But I emerged from all of that more determined than ever before to never be silenced.

∽

I've been asked this question over and over again: How did I survive that? What kept me going? What did I hold on to? Different variations of the same question.

I write this book to answer just that.

My story does not start with me. The courage—or resilience or whatever you want to call it—that I was able to display did not come to me overnight. My strength is inherited. I don't believe that my existence is all about a three-day-long controversy. My story does not begin there and it does not end there, which is why this book is not about that.

I write about two generations of women in my family who fought their own battles, who stood by each other and who kept going, no matter what. I grew up with these women, listening to their stories over and over again and watching them take on the world on their own terms. I want to tell you about them.

I was only a few weeks short of turning three when I lost my father. I do not have a lot of memories of him and I never had the chance to get to know him on my own, but he lives on in our hearts. In this book I will tell you everything that I remember about him. These are memories I've kept close to my heart for a very long time. I go over them again and again, every single day. There have been no car rides during which my thoughts have not gone back to those days.

In this book, I write them all out, every single image that I have. To the whole world, my dad was an officer who lost his life in the service of the country. In this book, you will meet the young boy, the officer, the son, the brother, the loving husband . . . and the father. Everyone remembers the day of his funeral, when he was wrapped in the *tiranga* (tricolour), decorated with strings of marigolds, saying goodbye to us all. But the few memories that I have of him were very difficult to write and even more difficult to share.

I started reading books when I was very young. A teacher got me into the habit, and I will forever be thankful to her for that. In books, I found solace. While TV was teaching me how to hate, highlighting the differences between caste, gender, community and religion, teaching my young mind about the existence of 'the other', books taught me about experiences, life, loving and forgiving, blurring the lines between me and them. When I read books, I was no more the only kid, the special case; in those books, there were many like me, telling me that I wasn't the only one feeling the things I felt.

I never had friends in school. When I look back and try to find a reason for it, I can never quite put my finger on one thing. I could just never have the conversations the other kids had. I could never attend birthday parties. My mother was so busy with work that scheduling play dates was never a priority. I made conversations awkward when kids talked about what they did over the weekend with their families, and somewhere along the way I stopped trying to fit in.

The library in my school was not open to students below class V, but I begged my librarian every day for weeks till she let me in. And ever since that day, I spent my lunch hours with comics or magazines or books, like Roald Dahl's *Matilda*. On the day I told her that I was leaving to go to a boarding school, she went to the restricted shelves of the library and came back with a book in her hand. It was an old hardbound copy of *Little Women*. She told me the story reminded her of my sister and me. It was the first time I had read a book I could relate to. It was about four young girls who lived alone with their mother while their father was out fighting the war. I still have the copy with me and the book has a special place in my heart and on my bookshelf. I understood that I was not the only girl who lived like this and that provided me comfort.

At eleven years, I wrote the first chapter of this book. I knew I wanted to share my story. I thought to myself, 'Maybe there will be a young girl for whom my story will resonate, and maybe someday I'll write a book that will make her feel less alone.'

Over the years, the book has changed its shape. I realized that I could not tell the story of my father and me without telling the story of my mother. I cannot talk about love, strength and forgiveness without going back to where I learnt how to love, be strong and forgive.

My father is as alive as he was back when I was only a child and it is because of my mother who has never let us feel his absence. My house is full of his pictures; our evenings are full of conversations about him; his presence in our life is never lost.

In this book, I don't talk about the incident where you think my story began. I talk, instead, about the events that led to the incident.

1

Gurmehar, Age Three
Jalandhar, 7 August 1999

I don't understand the chaos. The house is full of people, some whom I know and some whom I don't. I recognize my family, these are faces that I've seen before. There is Jackie Chachu there and Pawan here. On any other day it would have been routine, nothing out of the ordinary, as they are always at home for a game of carom, sprawled out on the living room floor, sipping on their chai, laughing loudly at jokes I don't understand.

But today they are not happy. No one is laughing.

The elders in the house told me that Papa would come home today. Yet, I can see everybody in the house but him. I look for him. My eyes go over everyone's sad faces one by one, hoping to find him in the room full of people, wondering if I have missed him, wondering if he is here looking for me too and cannot find my tiny body lost in the crowd.

I am about to ask people, I am about to call out to him, but by then, with a sea of mourning people and men in uniform, he comes back. He comes back sleeping in a wooden box, with a bandage on his chest—on the same spot where I used to lean my tiny head against and sleep, listening to the rhythm of his heartbeat.

My father is finally home.

ᔕ

I don't understand how he can sleep amidst all this noise and crying. People are taking his name over and over again, but he does not wake up. I hold the edges of the wooden box to look closer, propped on my knees, trying to keep a balance as the crowd gathers around me to take another look. These people bother me, they are not letting my papa sleep. I turn around in anger to ask them to be quiet, but I see a lady behind me, crying loudly and beating her chest, and I start crying out of fear. There is uncertainty and unfamiliarity in the air. Everyone seems to know something that I don't.

I call out to Papa softly, hoping he will listen to me. I know that he will wake up at the sound of my voice. I am his special little girl. He doesn't wake up.

I want to go away. I want to be somewhere safe and happy. I want to go back home, to the place where whenever Papa came we were happy. Mummy isn't here with me. She is in the other corner, across from me, staring at Papa, unable to hold back her tears as her chest heaves with uncontrollable sobs. I walk towards her on my knees. I want her to hold me and comfort me, I want her to take me away from here.

'Mummy!' The words barely fall out of my mouth. She looks up from Papa's face to see me sitting on my heels, waiting for her to acknowledge my presence. This has not happened before—she always knows which corner of the room I am in. But not today. Today she notices no one around her, she understands nothing around her. Her eyes meet mine. She takes me in her arms, hugs me tight and cries in the little nook of my neck, painfully forming a sentence between the sobs: 'Papa is gone now, he won't come back home.'

What does she mean? I don't understand. Her words make no sense to me.

'Your father passed away. He died,' she says. The others say the same thing, but what do they mean? What is 'died'? What is 'death'? I let my questions be, they only make people cry more. Papa is still there in the box.

'Mummy, what is this?' I ask, pointing to the wooden box, curious to know what it is.

'It is a dream,' she says.

'Dream,' I repeat. The box is called a dream.

'Close your eyes. It will all go away. It's only a dream.' She holds me tighter. I close my eyes for a few seconds and then open them. The box is still there; it has not gone.

The men come in uniforms. So does Papa's brother, Chachu. Dadaji, his father, comes along with them. Chachu's eyes are filled with tears. Boys cry too.

They lift the dream—covered in the tricolour and dressed with marigolds whose faint smell stays behind on your wrists, fingers and palms—and take it away.

∽

'Will he not come back ever?' I ask Bhaiyya. Bhaiyya works in our house and helps with repairs, and also takes me to the shop to get Kit Kats. Everybody is with Mummy and Papa, but I have been asked to stay here. I hear gunshots outside—the twenty-one gun salute.

'You should be very proud of your father. He fought with the bad Pakistani people and died to save the country,' Bhaiyya says.

'I understand, but when will he wake up?' I ask.

As I see Chachu walking towards me, I remove my hands from Bhaiyya's neck and run towards him. He takes me in his arms. He runs his hand through my hair and tells me in his soft voice, 'Papa is there. I'm taking you to him.'

Papa is there. He is not in a dream any more; he is lying on the hay. His eyes are still closed. Mummy is standing next to him. Chachu puts me on the ground and I walk towards Mummy. Everybody clears the way for me, all eyes looking at me. Mummy picks me up and I can see Papa better. 'Look at him and remember him,' she whispers in my ears, her voice quivering. I lean forward and look at him.

He is there, in front of me, his face calm despite all the chaos around him. I stare at his face for the last time. I have to remember this image. I take in his hair, which I used to tug at whenever he gave me piggyback rides; his closed eyes, which he taught me how to kiss before saying goodnight; his nose, which he told me looked similar to mine; and his lips which were curled into a Mona Lisa smile. I remember it.

All I remember after that are flames. I look for him again. He was right there a few seconds ago and now he is gone.

2

Wazirabad, 1947

The word was out long before it was officially declared. It travelled in whispers from one ear to another, sparking debates and conversations about all the possibilities. They were going to break us into two nations, one for us and one for them. Punjab would be split in two—West Punjab was to be in Pakistan and East Punjab was to remain in India.

Amarjeet's family was fortunate enough to know what was going to happen after 15 August 1947. Her father was a senior officer in the Railways who was in direct contact with the people who were making this happen. They were to be free but this future freedom had a price—one that they would have to pay for leaving behind every trace of their past and moving forward with no legacy.

They were fortunate enough to know and to arrange for their travel before the others. It was never going to be as bad for them as it would be for the others. The whole family packed their bags with just the bare essentials as there wasn't much that could be carried across. There would be a border, a partition. There would be children born who would never be able to imagine this old India. The land that belonged to their families would lie on the other side of the barbed wire; it would no longer be home but just a memory.

Trains had begun leaving one after the other, each one with thousands of people. This was much more than what they could carry. The riots had begun. People were stuffed inside the trains like doomed chickens on their way to the butcher's. By the time they reached the last station, the coaches were carrying more dead bodies than live people.

'Babaji, what should I do about my tattoo?' Amarjeet's brother asked. He had a tattoo of a *kantha* on his arm, the symbol of Guru Gobind

Singh's Khalsa Panth. Word was going around that they were picking up Sikhs from the trains and butchering them.

'Should we put acid on his hand?' asked their mother. What else was there to do?

'There is no time. He will get an infection and die. Just pick up the essentials and move. The situation is only going to get worse. My colleagues are waiting for us at the railway station; they have got a coach reserved for us. I have also got a job transfer to Saharanpur. We are very lucky, don't worry. If it's in our kismet, then we will all die. There is nothing that can be done about it,' said their father.

That day the whole family left for India. The one they were now supposed to call their own.

3

Gurmehar, Age Six
Jalandhar, 2002

The market has two toyshops in the same lane, one next to the other. Mummy told me once that both the shops belonged to an old uncle when she was young, but after he died his sons decided to turn it into two different toyshops. I think it is a good thing because two is always better than one.

In the same lane there is an old store that constantly smells of petrol and has a neon board that screams out the shop's name. We give all our pretty winter clothes for dry cleaning to the uncle who sits on the counter. There is nothing that we love more than our trips to the market, especially this lane, because while we wait for the clothes to be ironed, Mummy lets us have popcorn or candyfloss from the shop next door. I really like eating candyfloss. I can never have the whole thing without it sticking to my whole face. I'm not the one to blame and I tell Mummy this. The fault completely lies with the size of the whole thing. It's double the size of my head and triple the size of Bani's—my sister's.

I have a plan and it almost always works. To get to the candyfloss shop from the drycleaners, we have to walk past the toyshop. I just have to be swift enough to enter one of them. It is a good thing that they don't have doors but a shutter that comes down when it is time for the shop to close. I just have to stand there, pick a doll and try really hard to convince Mummy to buy it for me. Sometimes it works, sometimes it doesn't. Convincing her is not as easy as it sounds.

∽

One day Mummy scolds me because I cannot write '5' properly. I get so angry at her. I do not want to talk to her or be around her. I go to Nani, my mother's mother, and tell her I do not like Mummy any more. 'Why can't she be sweet like you?' I ask her as I rub the tears from my eyes.

'No, don't talk about your mother like that. You don't know what she has given up to be with you and give you a happy life. This school that you go to, the new uniforms, the pencil boxes and the Barbie school bags that you have are all because of her. Never talk about your mother like that,' Nani says.

ꕥ

Nani has a special man who flies down from the land of the gods to give us chocolates, but only she knows where he will come to meet her. His favourite places are the high wall-hanging behind the door, the cupboards and the freezer of the fridge we cannot reach. Nani has one rule though: every time we want chocolates, we have to pray to him and keep our eyes closed. She warns us that if we ever try to be sneaky and open our eyes, Babaji will stop visiting. I never think that this is a risk worth taking.

ꕥ

I'm home from school. I really want the chocolates, but Nani gave me one for school today, and I know I won't get another one. There is no way to convince her; she will tell me about the two cavities that had to be filled last week. The doctor was kind enough to tell Mummy that almost all children of this age have cavities, but Nani wouldn't take that as an excuse.

It is funny because she is Mummy's mummy, so even Mummy has to listen to everything she says. I asked Mummy once why she never fought with Nani and loved her so much. She simply told me it was because there was no amount of love that could repay all that Nani had done for her and Maasi and that she would never ever disrespect her. 'Woman like Nani deserve to be praised all the time for their bravery,' Mummy says. I don't know much, but Mummy knows best, so I just agree. Besides, Nani is sweet and makes custard for snacks sometimes.

Right now, I have to find the chocolates. The bags behind the door might have them. I will need a chair to stand on because even though I can pull a bag down, I don't want to make a lot of noise, or Nani will wake up from her nap. The chair from the dining table can be easily dragged and makes very little noise.

I stand on the chair and look inside all the bags. One has a bunch of old keys that probably belong to the house in the village. Another bag has pieces of cloth, a sewing kit and a box of sewing needles. None of the bags has any chocolates. I find money in one, exactly fifty rupees. I can go to the shop and buy chocolate, but then I'm not allowed to cross the road on my own. These bags here are useless. The cupboard will definitely have them. But I will have to steal the cupboard keys. I shouldn't steal but then I really want the chocolates. I will just quietly take the keys from the drawer and hope Nani doesn't wake up.

Aha! The cupboard has some real gems. I've seen her keep all that she possessed and loved safely locked in this cupboard for years. It has a distinct smell to it, of old wood, cloth and hints of sickly sweet attar that her brother bought for her from a Dubai duty-free shop. We love him, he always comes back with a huge bag full of chocolates and goodies for all of us. Last time he got us a huge box full of pink rubber bands in all kinds of shapes and sizes, a beginner's eye shadow kit, a doll and dresses.

Everything is there the way I thought it would be. The single cupboard is stuffed with bags filled with little knick-knacks as well as important documents. None of the documents belong to Nani; most are ours and Mummy's. We don't know Nani's birthdate since there is no birth certificate or class X certificate even though we know she has completed class XII. Her English is impeccable and she speaks refined Hindi, Punjabi and Telugu.

The only certificate that really belongs to her is the one she keeps on the top shelf with Mummy's file and my nursery certificate file. There are two death certificates too, one is Nanaji's and one Papa's. I was told my papa died in a war called Kargil. The death certificate which I once read even states the date, 6 August, but I know that already. Every year, we observe *paath* at the local gurudwara for which we need to take leave from school. The leave form always says 'attending father's death anniversary'. I enjoy school a lot but I always dread this day—the long walk from my desk to the teacher's table with my diary in hand and in it a handwritten note dripped with sadness despite its curt language. What generally follows is pity on my teacher's face, a deep sigh of sympathy and a sad pat on the back.

The easiest way to reach the highest shelf is to step on the lowest shelf and climb up. I do just that. A big brown leather bag tumbles down with its contents flying across the room. A total disaster.

Knitting needles.

A watch.

An old pair of earrings.

An old pocket-sized photo album. All photos in black and white.

A file. Another file. Both old and grey.

A set of keys.

A dial.

A broken pair of spectacles.

A passport.

A passport? I look closer at the document. This is Nani's passport. I didn't even know she had a passport. I open it and examine it closely, curiously. And then I see it. The word next to 'birthplace' is 'Pakistan'.

I can sense my blood boiling. I want to tear that thing to pieces. Yet, I don't want to touch it. My mother has betrayed me. Why would we have the enemy's belongings inside our own house, locked and kept safe in the cupboard? It should have been burnt.

I scream.

The vase that was on the newly polished table is on the ground. The sharp pieces are scattered all over the room, along with Nani's belongings. *That woman's belongings.* She cannot be my *nani*, I cannot be her granddaughter. She is a Pakistani. From the same Pakistan that was responsible for the death certificate on the top shelf. I need to get her out. I don't think I can breathe any more. Rage pours down from my eyes because there is nothing that I can do.

I howl. My wails reach my mother and she comes rushing. I can hear her hurried footsteps on the staircase. She must think I have hurt myself. What do I tell her? I don't know what this emotion is that I'm feeling. It is painful but the wounds and bruises seem to be inside me.

I sleep next to her and I let her feed me. Why would they do this to me?

My mother is at the door, horrified. What separates me from her is the mess on the floor.

'Don't move, stay there. How did this happen? Did you do something?' she asks me as she quickly tries to pick up the broken pieces.

'You lied to me.'

'About what?'

Nani comes in. She is just as worried as Mom. This makes me cry louder. My nose starts running. I wonder where my handkerchief is. I make do with the back of my hands, rubbing the snot and the tears away in one painful smudge across my face.

'About Nani.'

Mummy has the passport in her hand along with the knitting needles, old keys and bits of the broken glass. She understands, so does *the woman*. She told me stories. Why did I listen to them? Mummy knows how I feel. We had a conversation on our way back from Saharanpur. She knows I hate them.

'Beta . . .' That's all that leaves her lips. *The woman*'s face falls as her eyes well up with tears. It is the two of us crying now. My wails overpower her silent tears and I know I've won because the louder I cry the more pain I project.

'I will tell you a story, but first you stop crying,' Mummy says. 'I know why you are angry and I know why you are crying.'

'Is Nani a Muslim too?'

'No, she is not. But even if she is, would it matter?'

'I don't believe you. You lied to me.'

'We never did.'

'She is a Pakistani. We have a Pakistani in our home.' I start crying louder at the word Pakistani.

'You don't believe me but do you believe in God?'

This is an easy question. I believe in God. I have to, only then will he listen to all my wishes.

My mother starts telling me a story.

∽

In 1704, Guru Gobind Singh Ji's Army of Sikhs fought with the Mughals. They called it the Battle of Anandpur Sahib. We Sikhs are the warrior clan. We fight for what is right and we rise up against the unjust. The battle had been brutal and many soldiers were dying. The Mughals had laid siege to the Sikhs so that no food or supplies could reach the Sikh soldiers. There was a shortage of food and water. The wounded, injured and dead men were all lying on the battleground bleeding, some struggling to breathe. The sun was at its absolute worst. The scorching heat was nature's way of torturing the injured soldiers. Among them was a man whose duty was to do *paani di sewa*. Every day, after the battle was fought and both armies moved back to their camps to rest, Bhai Kanhaiya Ji would start doing his job. He would walk around the bloodied battlefield looking for soldiers who were still breathing and give them water to quench their thirst. What was unusual was that he not only gave water to the Sikhs but also to the Mughal soldiers. This was not very well received by the Sikhs and they complained to Guru Ji about it.

'He is a traitor. We are fighting every day and he is going and reviving the enemy's men,' they complained to Guru Ji. Upon hearing this, Guru Ji summoned Bhai Kanhaiya Ji and asked him if the allegations were true.

'Yes, my Guru, what they say is true. But Maharaj, I saw no Mughal and Sikh on the battlefield. I only saw human beings. And Guru Ji, don't they all have the same God's spirit? Guru Ji, have you not taught us to treat all God's people as the same? Our Sikh heroes destroy the enemy by killing them, but I destroy the enmity by saving them.'

Guru Gobind Singh Ji smiled when he heard this. 'You have understood the true message of the Gurbani,' he told Bhai Kanhaiya Ji. 'From tomorrow, carry balms and mend the wounds of the soldiers too.'

~

'Papa did what he had to as a true Indian soldier. But you, beta, you have to do your part for the world, which is not the same as Papa's,' said Mummy after finishing the story. 'You have to be like Bhai Kanhaiya Ji. Serve humanity by killing enmity. Tomorrow, when you decide to be a soldier, then you will have to do your job, which is killing the enemy. Until you serve the nation in the uniform, you must continue to serve the human race.'

I have to go hug Nani. I was very rude to her. I don't care if she is a Pakistani, she is serving humanity.

'Is Nani a Pakistani?' I still ask for confirmation.

'No, she lived in Pakistan when there was no India or Pakistan, but just one big nation. Today she is as Indian as you and I.'

This makes me extremely happy but also guilty. I have to go say sorry to Nani. I run towards her room. She is sitting on her bed with her prayer beads, humming a constant murmur of 'Waheguru, Waheguru'. I go and hug her. I break her rhythm but she doesn't mind. I get smothered in hugs instead. 'I'm sorry, Nani. I'm a bad person. Please forgive me for making you cry,' I say, ashamed.

'We are all God's children and we all make mistakes,' she tells me. 'Do you want a chocolate?' I do want a chocolate. I was indeed looking for one in the first place. I won't tell her that though. She takes me along with her to a different cupboard and asks me to close my eyes and pray for a chocolate. She reminds me that I have to pray with a true and innocent heart, with honest intentions. The chocolate lands in my hands and I open my eyes.

4

Saharanpur and Vizag, 1970s

Amarjeet was not the name she was given at birth. Born on a bright spring day of March in a local hospital in Wazirabad, Pakistan, the beautiful child with soft curly hair was named Agya Rani. The name was considered very modern and chic by the rest of the family. Traditionally, parents did not choose the name of their child exclusively based on inclination. There was a process, which included a holy book, a holy man and a raffle draw of a lucky letter. Agya Rani was different.

The word 'agya' had two completely contrasting meanings depending on the context in which it was used. 'Permission' was what it would translate to in simple English. Giving permission was an act that implied that the person concerned was in a position of power and authority. Asking for permission was about submission: bowing one's head, folding hands, lowering the eyelashes and pleading. Rani, of course, meant 'queen'.

Our Agya belonged to the first category, but just before she got married, the groom's family decided it was better if she was called Amarjeet.

'Change her name to Amarjeet. What is this name Agya Rani? She is not a Hindu girl. If she has to be our bahu then she will have to follow the rules and regulations of our house. We are Sikhs, Bhaisaab, so the name has to belong to our religion,' said the boy's parents in panic-stricken, concerned tones. This was not a request or a condition; this was a test to check if the feisty young girl who sat quietly in the room, fidgeting, would bend to their wishes eventually.

'Bhaisaab, if that is what you want then your wish is our command,' agreed Agya's parents immediately. The young boy was six feet and three inches tall, an engineer with the vocabulary of an Englishman. *It is only a name,* they decided, and shook hands upon the union of the two parties.

'Amarjeet Kaur and Ajeet Singh,' both the parties said in unison, stuffing orange grainy motichoor ladoos in each other's mouths. *Dholkiwaalas* were asked to start playing and the entire village was signalled that the *rishta* was fixed. Amarjeet was going to marry Ajeet and somewhere amidst the sounds of dhol and squeaks of congratulatory laughter, Agya receded back into her shell and this new girl, a shadow, a synonym of Ajeet, stepped in.

∽

The sun was hanging low on the horizon, dipping in the eastern sea somewhere on the coast of Vizag, where Amarjeet and Ajeet lived with their two daughters, Pammi and Raji. Being a senior engineer in the newly formed government had its perks. A beautiful house near the coast was one of them. Money wasn't in excess but it was enough, and the whole family travelled comfortably on their Chetak scooter. Raji, the baby of the house, would stand in front, their dad in control of the scooter, with their mother in the backseat and Pammi somehow squeezed between her mother and father. This was a strange arrangement but the family wouldn't have it any other way. The weather was kind and to the girls nothing was more fun than their weekly trips to the bazaar as they cruised along the shore with the sea breeze blowing in their face, hoping, that if they behaved, they would be treated to a scoop of pineapple ice cream each.

Amarjeet had a list of things that she needed to restock every now and then, and fish was a priority. It also included drumstick, rava, dosa rice, tamarind, besan and occasionally ground coffee, since Ajeet would sometimes want his masala chai to be replaced with south Indian filter coffee on days when the workload was more. She did not go to work despite being well qualified. Instead, she spent her time dressing up both her daughters in cotton frocks and dresses which she stitched whenever inspiration hit her. There was comfort in these mundane domestic acts and she wanted nothing more than to raise two smart, beautiful girls and to be able to provide for them, emotionally. Her childhood was taken away from her the day she left the house she and her brother grew up in.

She often thought about her childhood home and wondered if the peepul tree was still there in their courtyard and if the owners were kind enough to not paint over the doodles they had drawn on the walls. Maybe they had painted over it and now somewhere in the enemy's land was a piece of her childhood, painted over with multiple layers of paint.

Both her elder brothers were settled in Britain after graduating from IITs. The brothers loved their Agya to bits and her daughters even more. Every three months they would send a courier to the girls with the latest clothes and toys from England and every time it arrived, the air would be filled with excitement and nervous energy.

Their library was stocked with children's books and magazines from England. They would spend hours looking at the pictures even though they couldn't read properly. The same magazines became the source of fashion inspiration for Amarjeet.

A master tailor with hands that created magic, she would often stitch a dress or two for her neighbours, David and his mother, as Christmas presents, and in return they would get fresh, home-made cakes. Christmas and New Year's Eve were celebrated along with Diwali and

Guru Purab with equal enthusiasm and love. Who cared what festival it was? It was about food, new clothes and parties where everyone came together.

5

Gurmehar, Age Eight
Jalandhar, 24 December 2004

I love coming to Dadi's house. She is Papa's mother. Dadi loves to eat dhokla but every time she tries making it, it falls flat and doesn't get the fluffy cake-like consistency it is supposed to have. I enjoy Dadi's food more than the food at home. I've heard so much about '*maa ke haath ka khaana*' from my friends in class. My mother makes great food but it is usually a weekend affair as she is busy with work on weekdays. Nani and Bhaiyya are the ones who cook at home. Nani always makes green vegetables and yellow dal to keep us healthy while Dadi spoils us with buttery paranthas and jeera pulao with bowls of special raita. They tell me this was Papa's favourite combination. My way of staying close to Papa is to like everything he liked. I sit on his chair on the dining table and eat from his favourite plate.

I enjoy putting make-up on the doll and dressing her up. Mummy doesn't dress up or wear make-up but she has a whole box full of it in the cupboard. I take it out occasionally and practise on my face. Unlike real life where I end up looking like a clown, my character in the computer game looks perfect.

'Do you know what date it is tomorrow?' My cousin Shweta asks me.

'Yes, it is a holiday because of Christmas,' I say. Shweta and I are in the same school but she is older and her class is in a different building.

'Does Santa give you gifts?' she asks.

'No, I don't know how to ask. My friend tells me that there is a magic spell that you have to say.'

'There is no spell, you just have to hang socks in white, red or green with a letter asking for what you want. Then Santa comes and takes the letter away and puts toys in place of it.'

I run back to Dadi's house where Mummy and Dadi are sitting and having chai and dhokla, laughing about something. 'Mummy, we have to go home *right now*!' I tug at her arm, begging her to leave. I never want to leave Dadi's house but today I have to go back so that I have time to write a letter and find the perfect sock.

'Beta, wait! We will go in a while. We are still eating,' Mummy tells me.

'No, no, no, that is not how it works. We have to go home now so that Santa can come tonight,' I say and it seems like she finally gets it.

'Give us fifteen minutes and we will go?'

Mummy is being very annoying. She has to go to the dry-cleaners again and we are getting late.

'Why don't you go to the toyshop and wait while I'm settling the bill?' she says at the dry-cleaners.

'Okay,' I say and take Bani with me.

'Bani, what do you want from Santa?' I ask her at the store and she looks at the remote control car. 'I want a Barbie, the one whose ad comes on TV,' I tell her, looking at all the Barbie dolls placed on the shelf.

Mummy comes to take us back and has no bag in her hand.

'Where are the clothes?'

'Oh, they aren't done yet. I only had to pay.' She smiles and takes my hand. 'Don't you want to buy a small Christmas tree for Santa to place the toys under?' she asks.

We go back home with a huge tree and fairy lights of different colours. Mummy decorates the Christmas tree while Bani and I spend all our time writing letters and finding the perfect sock. Eventually, we decide to take the new pair of school socks and hang them. They are white in colour—it should work.

'You know, there is another rule. When we were kids, Santa used to visit us too. The rule is that you can't stay up the whole night waiting for Santa. He won't come if you do. So quickly go and sleep,' Mummy tells us.

We fall asleep even though it is one of the most difficult things to do.

~

There are two gifts placed right under our tree. I go to check my sock and find that the letter is gone. Instead, there are chocolates and candy there. I scream with joy and wake Mummy and Bani up.

'Look, Santa came to our house too!' I can't contain my happiness as I open my gifts.

6

Vizag, 1970s

It was the day he was supposed to leave. Mentally, they were all ready—the promises of daily phone calls from phone booths and returning home with suitcases full of gifts for the girls were made as consolation. These were little tricks they used to comfort each other, to get over the pain of separation. It was almost like acting in a play. There was a script everyone had to follow despite how they were actually feeling because if one person broke down they would all follow suit. Ever since their wedding, Amarjeet and Ajeet had never been apart. It was a daunting idea for her to live without her husband, it worried her.

At least he would come back every six months. She kept repeating this in her head. It was important to act strong in front of the kids. If she started crying, then they would too and where would a crying woman with two crying daughters go?

The suitcases and trunks were packed. Their father's name written with white paint on the trunks had dried and was ready for the long journey to Ahmedabad. The achaar and paranthas were wrapped in a cloth and kept in a jute basket. Lunch ended sooner than they would have liked. They were counting every moment and now it was time. After clearing the dining table and putting away the leftovers in the refrigerator, Ajeet and his friends put the trunks in the back of the car and the girls waited, longingly looking at their father from under their moist lashes, trying to hold back tears, their chest heavy with sadness. They were taught not to cry when this day came. They were told they had to be strong. So they held back their tears with all their might while their lips quivered at the thought of an emptier house.

The train was on time, a rare and unfortunate event when they had all wished for a delay.

'We will miss you, Papa.'

'I will miss you too. Don't cry. You will be good girls, strong girls. You both will take care of your mother and never give her any trouble. You will also always go out of your way to help her,' he told them.

His friends put their hand on his shoulder and assured him that his kids would be taken care of.

'Don't worry, we will take the girls for a movie and they will forget about all this,' his friends tried to comfort him.

'Don't spoil them too much when I'm gone,' he warned them and smiled as he climbed the steps to his coach.

It was a sunny morning when Amarjeet came back from the phone booth with a spring in her step and a mithai *dabba* in her hand. 'He is getting transferred,' she yelled from the gate of the house. Pammi and Raji couldn't believe their ears. Was he getting transferred back here? Were they finally going to be together again? No more empty chairs on the dinner table, no more awkward silences when they all expected to hear his voice and it didn't come.

'When is he coming back?' asked the girls.

'He will be here in a week and we need to pack. We are all going to Nangal,' she said.

Their faces dropped. They didn't want to leave the house at all. They loved it here. The sea, the sand and the fish. 'Where is Nangal?' they asked

'It's very close to our house in the north. Don't worry, Nangal is beautiful. There are hills where we can go for picnics. It will be lovely,' Amarjeet said.

Ajeet came back a few days later, with toys for both of them. These gifts made up for all the lost time. Their initial plan was to be mad at him, cry and tell him how terrible he was for leaving them alone here, but then they saw the toys and their father's face and all their anger evaporated into thin air. All they could feel was intense love and a sense of relief. Finally, he was back. One of the toys was a camel which blew bubbles and the other was a boat.

The air in Nangal was different, less salty and much lighter. They couldn't remember ever having seen hills in real life—it was the first time. They had seen it in movies and in advertisements in the newspaper. It was surreal to be able to be this close to them in real life. Throughout the train journey, both of them made plans of climbing the hills.

'We will have races and see who climbs the hill first.'

'Yes. I've heard that you can see the whole world from the top of the hill, as far as England.'

'No, not as far as England. To see that far you need to climb the Mount Everest.'

'Arre, *toh* that is the plan. We will climb small hills here and prepare ourselves for Mount Everest. And when we are ready, we will climb that too, and from there we will wave at Mamaji in England!'

Even the roads were carved out of small hills, which made them think of these as roller coasters. The car would go up and then down and when that happened, something in their stomach would turn. Their parents were worried that they would get sick from all the travelling but that was far from the case. In their heads, they were already imagining playing on these roads, climbing up and rolling down on their stomachs. Nangal seemed like a long vacation.

What took them by surprise was the size of the house. The house in Vizag had been enormous, but this one was even bigger. It had a huge garden attached to it. The girls had never seen these many flowers before. The coast barely had any flowers, but here every piece of soil contained a flower of a different kind. There were roses and daffodils and bougainvilleas. The house had creepers running all across the wooden windows. Against the dull paint of the government quarters, the flowers looked even more vibrant.

Amarjeet could already imagine the picnics she would organize with the whole family on Sundays; they wouldn't even have to go anywhere. The neighbourhood was nothing like the one the girls had grown up in. The similarity between the neighbours' accent and their own mother's was the first thing they noticed. Unlike Vizag, where their mother had to get accustomed to speaking in a particular accent and where most of her conversations seemed rehearsed, now every word seemed to flow effortlessly.

The bags were taken inside and the dusting started. There wasn't much to do since the furniture was yet to arrive. Tonight, they would all sleep on the mattress they had brought with themselves. The bathrooms had proper fittings, even a shower—a little luxury. The city of the Bhakra Nangal Dam could afford showers. The grime from the three-day-long train journey would be washed off under simulated rain. This was like a dream. So what if there wasn't a beach? There was a shower!

That night, their little family sat in a restaurant and feasted on simple roti and dal with ice cream and some chai to wrap the whole day up.

'Happiness in a teacup,' their father said, lifting the little cup of chai in the air.

7

Gurmehar, Age Four
Jalandhar, 2000

There are things that people say about home.

What is a home? I often wonder. In our school, we have a book on it filled with cartoons. There are cartoons of 'Papa', 'Mummy', 'sister/brother' and 'me'. All of them live in a house. In the stories that the teacher reads out to us, they live in different places—clouds, jungle, city, farm and sometimes even under the sea. In all these stories, the house is made of different materials—ice, leaves, wood and my favourite, chocolates and biscuits. We have to read out from the book in class. The teacher points at one of the figures and we have to tell who it is.

'Who is this?' she asks, pointing a finger at something in the book.

'Papa bear,' we say in unison, huddled over the table in groups of five.

'Who is this?' she asks, her finger moving further, gliding across the glossy, colourful page of the book that taught us about family.

'Mama bear!' we say.

'Who are these?' She points at the little bears.

'Baby bears!' we say.

'Where do they live?' she asks, her finger on a structure drawn in the book.

'Happily in a house,' we yell. This usually means the end of the exercise and we can go out to the ground and play with our friends.

I don't like this time, especially after this exercise. I don't like a lot of things. It's not a very nice feeling to have, Mummy tells me, but it cannot be helped. I also find it difficult to understand a lot of things these teachers teach. It's very hard to relate to. Everyone in the class silently nods while my mind tries hard to connect the dots. In my house, there is Mama bear, Baby bear and Me-bear, but there is no Papa bear. At this point, I have doubts, which I don't know how to put into words. So I choose not to ask the teacher, but in the hollow of my chest this doubt rests, digging its roots deep. If home is a place where Papa bear and his family lives together happily, then I believe I will never be home. They tell me that he will not come back. They repeat it to me over and over every time I ask about his whereabouts, but what do they mean when they say he won't come back? What is this place that sucks humans in and holds them there forever? In my head, it's behind huge iron gates. Every day the image of the place changes.

During the break after our study activity, I often sit near the sandbox and wonder what this place would look like. I want to go and see it but I'm afraid it will suck me in too and I won't ever come back, but I would at least find Papa there. I don't fear this place that people go to and never come back. I fear this place where people have to survive each and every day on memories of two and half years, holding on to them for the rest of their lives, however long they live. I secretly hope mine isn't too long, for I'd rather be with him.

I tell Mummy this. She breaks down into tears and asks me to never utter such words again. I tell her that she should come with me to this place that people don't come back from. She says she wishes she could.

I realize I need a plan. I do not trust these adults. They cry and are unreliable. Who can be sure that they know what they are talking about? On the one hand Mummy tells me that if I close my eyes and try to talk to him he will be able to hear me; on the other hand she tells me he won't come back. On the one hand she tells me he loves me unconditionally; on the other hand she tells me he still won't come back. If he loves me, he will come back, he just doesn't know where to come.

My gut instincts know better—I know that if I go to Dadi's house, he will be there. Maybe no one told him our new address. My mother and Dadi had a little tiff before we moved here, so maybe she is keeping Papa with her.

My old buggy uncle still comes to the school, but I now have a new buggy that takes me to the new house. I sit and wonder if my old buggy will take me back to my old home.

'Today, after school, I will quietly go and sit in the old buggy. No one will find out—it is always overcrowded,' I think.

My heart is fluttering. I cannot contain my excitement. The watch is ticking even though I'm not sure how to read it. There is the bigger finger and the smaller finger and then there is my favourite, the fastest ticking finger. The faster the time goes, the better. I have often seen my teachers glance at the clock in the middle of the class, usually when we become too troublesome.

At the last parent–teacher meeting, my teacher told my mother that I was either too chatty or extremely quiet. Mummy came home and asked me about it. I told her that there were times when I didn't have much to say because no one understood me. My life was foreign to me, yet it was my own. I learnt soon that not many kids were interested in it. They made faces. She told me that people made faces at things they didn't understand.

'But adults know everything,' I retorted.

She said, 'You'd be surprised to know that even they are as clueless or sometimes even more.'

School ends for the day and we proceed towards our respective buggies and autos. I look around to see if anyone is watching. I put my books, *Learning ABC* and *Counting Numbers till 100*, in my bunny bag and zip it up as casually as I can. No one should suspect anything. I walk, taking small steps towards the gate. Then I break into a run and swiftly jump into my old buggy. Mission accomplished.

ᔕ

The buggy uncle looks very surprised. He comes up to me and asks me to go to my new buggy. I refuse.

How did he notice me sitting there, I wonder. I had put my head down and was sitting in the corner. He shouldn't have been able to see me.

My new buggy uncle is also there, asking me to go with him. I have made up my mind. I will not go with him. I have been living in the new house for too long that I haven't seen my dadi or my *chachus* in a long time. I want to go back. I want to go back to a life that was mine. It's so difficult to adapt to change; I simply don't want to. I will do everything I can to have the life I want.

I have my hands gripped tight on the buggy windows as they try to pull me away. The window is cutting against my hand. I'm crying. It's painful but I won't leave. I scream louder. The mucus running down my nose goes into my mouth.

I cry louder. They try to pull me from my waist. I screech louder. 'I want to go to my papa,' I cry out.

They finally give up and let me sit in the buggy.

I see my teachers talking to my buggy uncle. All my friends are staring at me. I'm hot with embarrassment and tears but it all subsides when I realize I have won. I wipe my nose and eyes with my hands. My hands are moist. I wipe it with my skirt. My skirt becomes dirty but it can be washed. There is no big damage as long as things can be repaired, fixed and revived. From this point on, I will revive everything. Bhaiyya is back and he asks me if I'm okay. I'm more than okay. I haven't been this okay in a very long time. I'm finally going home.

∽

I jump out of the buggy and run towards Dadi's house through the streets I call my own, not the strange ones I've had to play on since we moved out. Papa would walk on these streets with me on his shoulder, late in the evening post dinner. He would point to the hoardings and tell me about the actresses on them.

The iron gates of the house are a bit too high for my reach, so I ring the bell and wait. Chachu comes out but he doesn't look surprised. I had thought that they would all be surprised and ecstatic. This reaction is mildly disappointing. I walk behind him into the house towards the drawing room. I know my way well and I walk here with a certain confidence.

To my shock, Mummy is sitting on the sofa with Dadi and Dadu.

There is tension in the air. I think they have just had a discussion. I've seen them have a lot of such discussions lately, resulting in a terrible mood, after which we moved to our new house. This is the first time I'm meeting Dadi since their last discussion. Mummy never tells me about them. Every time I ask her, she dismisses the question or answers in monosyllables.

'When will we go back to our house?'

'Soon.'

'I want to go to Dadi.'

'Not now.'

Here I am, a defiant little child figuring my way to get what I want but no one in that room seems happy. I realize that I shouldn't have done what I did. I prepare myself for confrontation.

'Why did you come here?' Mummy asks me. I sense trouble.

'I missed this house,' I say honestly. I cannot lie. Lies are hard.

As I say this, Dadi and Mom break into tears and so do I. Dadi gets up and hugs me. My dadi is a tight hugger. I can feel my bones dig into my own flesh every time she hugs me. She hugs with all her strength, trying to pour every ounce of love from her body into mine. The science behind it is unknown but it certainly works.

'Go hug your mom,' she tells me as she loosens her embrace. I look at Mummy sheepishly. I know every expression on her face. I know what she is trying to tell me by looking into her eyes. It's a secret language that only we both know. She approves. I go and hug her. Suddenly, everything seems fine and the tension in the air evaporates. Chachu cracks a joke and everyone giggles just a little bit. It's our little family after all, bound by blood and unconditional love for someone who will never return.

Papa isn't here. I tell everyone about my plan and the motivation behind it. They stare at each other as I tell the story, but as soon as I finish they promise me that I am welcome any time I want to come and to stay for as long as I like. But I will have to go back with Mummy today. I agree. I learn their phone number by heart. I am assured that they will come home or pick me up from my new house whenever I call.

I don't find Papa but I have a feeling I have found something that needed to be found.

8

Nangal, 1970s

The phone rings in the other room as all of them sit together at the dining table to eat breakfast. It was idli and sambar that day, a south Indian delicacy that travelled with them from Vizag. It was a hassle-free dish to cook for Amarjeet and she loved the fact that the sambar could be saved up for lunch to serve with rice. Many of her new neighbours found this dish to be quite strange. Amarjeet rushed to pick up the phone, wiping her wet hands on her dupatta that was secured across her waist.

It wasn't the kind of news she wanted to hear first thing in the morning. Pammi and Raji's bus driver had called to let them know that he wouldn't be able to pick them up for school. This meant speeding up the morning routine so that Ajeet could get time to drop them on his way to work.

For Pammi and Raji, this was anything but bad news; this meant reaching school before everyone else and getting to sit on the best seats, the ones in the front, closest to the teacher and the blackboard.

It made Amarjeet extremely happy that they were doing well and had no problems adjusting in the new environment. Life here was different and good, a little too good to be true. It almost felt like a dream they would wake up from any day. With idlis in their stomachs and tiffin boxes, the three of them left for school on the scooter.

The arrangement was the same. Raji, the younger and shorter one, would stand in front and Pammi would sit behind with her hands around her dad's waist. 'Tightly' was non-negotiable as her little body would otherwise lose its balance when the scooter twisted and turned around the Nangal hills. Ajeet would put a baby helmet on Pammi's tiny head, with two ponytails tied with school ribbons hanging from the sides, and make sure that her arms were fastened around him. Pammi did not enjoy wearing the helmet but loved the scooter rides with her dad. It was one of the best things in life.

∽

The girls had been dropped off, kisses on their cheeks planted and goodbyes said. Ajeet had a long day of work to look forward to. He had to supervise the work at a construction site. There was a lot to be done, but he expected to finish all his work by afternoon and go home for lunch instead of eating the cold idlis. He had to pick the girls up from school anyway. If he managed to finish everything here before that, he might not even have to go back in the evening. Maybe they could all go to the club, he wondered.

He couldn't wait to get home.

∽

'She is the most beautiful teacher I have ever seen,' Pammi kept thinking, watching her new teacher write on the blackboard. Her voice was musical. The sun outside was shining and the lawns were greener than usual. She was so lost in her own thoughts that she didn't notice the two men who had come to the class and were talking to the teacher. The teacher called out her name, but she didn't hear it. The students started giggling and pointing her out to the teacher. The teacher however did not find any of this funny.

'Parvinder, go with them,' she told Pammi.

'Why, ma'am?' She was taught not to go with strange men anywhere. It was important to ask why.

'Your dad is calling you,' one of the two men said.

Pammi quietly went with the men. On the way, they asked her which class Raji was in. 'Why do you want to take her too?' she asked.

'It is because your dad is calling both of you,' came the reply. Their voices were unnaturally heavy, almost sad. Pammi walked in front of them to show them the way to Raji's class.

Raji looked up from her desk as the teacher called out her name and asked her to leave with them. She looked at Pammi, who looked at her and nodded. A green signal that she could go. She packed her bag slowly, one pencil at a time. All eyes were on her—it wasn't every day that kids were called from in between their classes and asked to leave. She doubted if this was a punishment but the strangeness of this whole thing made both of them extremely uncomfortable.

⁂

The building was beautifully structured and coming along very well, Ajeet thought as he went through the blueprints in his makeshift on-location cabin. In a few hours he would go and check with the labourers to see if everything was fine and if the cement was enough. The project had been budgeted well, so a shortage shouldn't be a problem.

Government projects were always well funded but it was the corruption at the higher level that they could do nothing about. Funds were needed to buy safety equipment and gear, and this was usually the money that went as bribe. Ajeet took the last sips of his chai, which was a little stronger and sweeter than he would have liked, picked up his helmet from the table and got going.

Site checks are regular procedures, an everyday thing, also one of the more fun aspects of his job. There was a kick to seeing something being built from the scratch, brick by brick, and to knowing that you were a part of the project. He made a mental note to check the crane that day. It was giving some trouble though he had been told that it was fixed.

It was swinging.

He saw it the moment he stepped out. He knew it wasn't right. The cranes never went out of control like that unless there was something wrong. He knew the labourers working right underneath couldn't see it, so he ran.

'Move out!' he yelled as he pushed the labourers away.

The load snapped from the crane. It was too late for him to move.

The car journey with the two men was uncomfortable as no one told them why they were being summoned home. All they knew was that their dad had called them. As they pulled into the driveway, they saw that the house was crowded. Pammi thought she knew what had happened. All of a sudden she was worried for her mother.

Amarjeet was in the hospital last month because of a viral fever that wouldn't go down and a crowd like this could only mean that she fell extremely ill again.

'Where is my mummy?' Pammi asked, worried.

'She is fine. We are taking you to her,' the men said.

To both of them, the whole day was a blur. The movements of the people were a blur. The mourning in the house was a blur. The wails were muffled sounds. They didn't know what confusion was until this day. No one told them anything but everyone said something.

Pammi could see people coming into the house, one after the other. Even the Ramleela group was there. Pammi loved the Ramleela story. The courage of Ram, the bond of brotherhood between him and Lakshman, the victory of good over evil—she had learnt so much from it.

But that day, Sita was there, in her own house. She was sitting on the other end of the room, across from her dad. Pammi's eyes couldn't leave her—she couldn't believe Sita had come to her house.

[illegible]

[illegible]

"Where is my [illegible]

[illegible]

[illegible] the whole day [illegible]

[illegible]

[illegible]

The courage of [illegible]

[illegible]

But the [illegible]

[illegible] had come to her [illegible]

9

Gurmehar, Age Three
Jalandhar, 1999

We have shifted to a new house with Nani and Bani. Mummy tells me that this will be our new home. There is a huge park right opposite the house and we are allowed to go there, but I really miss Dadi and Chachu. Dixie the dog also lives with us. She is a cute white Pomeranian who doesn't play with us a lot. I ask Mummy why and she tells me that it is because she is old and does not want to move. This reminds me of the time when I asked where Nani's husband was and Mummy replied that Nani didn't have one because she was old.

'She is old like Nani?' I ask about Dixie.

'Yes.'

'Is that why she doesn't have a husband too?'

'Yes.'

'In the old house, Shweta's mummy was telling someone that you don't have a husband now.'

'I don't.'

'Are you old too?'

Mummy doesn't quite seem to like my question. These days she doesn't really like anything at all. We used to play with stamps when we lived in Nani's house but when I ask her to make those stamps again she refuses and says she is tired. She has started going to office wearing ugly clothes. I do not like her clothes any more. In the evening, the park in front of our new house is filled with aunties who seem to be about her age. I once rode the see-saw with one of their kids. They have husbands, and they also dress in better clothes and wear lipstick and bindis. They look pretty. Mummy used to be pretty too but now her face looks plain. I told her that one day but she didn't like that either. All she likes now is to come home and sleep. Or eat ice cream—which she doesn't give us.

I don't like this house. Everything I do seems to upset Mummy. I tell her that. Sharp and clear. This house feels empty compared to the beautiful chaos of our previous house, Nani's village house and Dadi's house in the city.

Nani's house was tiny but it was beautiful, filled with old cupboards with intricate designs that I would run my fingers along all day. The cupboard had a set of bangles hanging on a clothes hanger. In the same cupboard, she kept piles of glittery, colourful clothes. Some were just materials waiting to be stitched, while some were beautiful suits in all colours of the rainbow. Her make-up was neatly arranged on the old dressing table, which had a shelf that creaked at its hinges. I loved opening and closing it and listening to it creak; it was musical, almost therapeutic.

The contents of that dressing table are now kept boxed in Tupperware containers in the cupboard. No one wears the make-up any more, neither Nani nor Mummy. I want to. It used to be my favourite pastime to sit and watch my mother put on her lipstick and bindi every morning. I would sit on the corner of the bed and look at her in awe. She would even let me decide the colours. I always liked the pink and red ones. She preferred the dark browns. Her collection of magazines would lie beside her as she tried to recreate the looks in them. Make-up was art to her back then.

She doesn't wear make-up any more, but yesterday I saw her bring home a bag full of painting brushes and watercolours. That evening, she practised drawing flowers, roses. I asked her why.

'They are easy and they represent love. When there is no love in life you need to create some for yourself,' she told me.

I did not understand a word of what she said. Mummy does that sometimes, she says things I don't understand. I don't even think she is saying them to me. She is just saying them out loud and I happen to be there, listening. She talks about Papa a lot. She keeps asking me if I remember him and what I remember about him.

'What are the pictures that come to your mind when I take his name?' she asks. I start recounting all my memories—images of him on his bike, images of him playing with the dog, images of him driving us to the amusement park. She tells me everything she remembers and together we start putting pieces of him back together in the hope of bringing him to life.

She then asks me, 'What do you remember about that day? Tell me the whole story.' I tell her. This is our evening schedule.

'He is not coming back, remember this well.'

'Why is he not coming back?'

'Because he died fighting for the country. Not many people do that. We are very proud of him. It was his duty, his love for his motherland and his love for his people, and this should never make you sad.'

I'm used to having things said at me rather than to me. It is my job to understand them. I have to use my mind a little bit harder. I watch a lot of television. I watch movies too. Old people die in movies and are then burnt just like Papa.

Papa's things are in a trunk that came back with him from the Valley and we have kept it in a special spot in our house. The trunk came with us when we moved to the new house and on the day we were moving, when the sun was hanging low in the sky, painting it a beautiful orange colour, we decided to open it to see what it had. Mummy went to the room to get the keys for the lock, pulled a cushion for herself and I sat on the floor cross-legged.

The trunk opened and the room filled with a familiar smell—the smell of him. It almost felt like he was home.

In the days that followed his death, everyone around was very sad and everyone cried. By now, I know that I'm supposed to cry when someone mentions Papa. I don't always want to. Most of the time I just want to talk about him. It is really sad that every time I start doing that, people who come to visit us stop talking and the air in the room gets slightly stiffer.

'How are you doing, Gulgul?' an aunty asks.

'I'm very well. How are you?' I say cheerfully. No one expects that. The cheerfulness.

'Beta, don't ever be sad. We are all there for you. We are your family, just like your mom and dad,' they say.

'Thank you, uncle and aunty, but I already have my mom and my dad,' I reply.

This is my mistake. I had forgotten that Papa had 'died' and when someone dies you have to become sad at the mention of their name. I had been so used to Papa not being around that this did not seem different. He was away fighting all the time anyway. Mummy used to tell me that he had to go to the Valley, that there were men there he needed to protect us from and that he would be back soon. I just had to be patient. Now she tells me that he will not come back, that he has gone to heaven to be with God.

So what if he is in the Valley or with God or in heaven? I will just go and bring him back. When they tell me where he is, they point to the sky.

'Where does God live?' I ask. Confused, sad eyes look at my tiny face and tell me that He lives up in the sky where the heavens are.

The sky doesn't seem too far. All I have to do is climb up the Nishan-saab in the gurdwara like the Bhaijis. I assume the Bhaijis know God well. We go to the gurdwara to make wishes and the Bhaijis sit in the tiny chair of the Nishan-saab and go to the top to reach God. There are a lot of kirpans in the gurdwara. It is not a difficult thing to do. I will sit in the Nishan-saab's little trolley chair and go to the top with a kirpan, tear the sky open and get Papa back from God.

Our house is full of Papa's pictures. Each and every wall. He is everywhere and yet nowhere. Sometimes I keep looking at the door, waiting, hoping for him to come back. Deep in my heart I know he will. He loves us, he could not have left us like this. It's a strange feeling, this uneasiness. I don't cry when I talk about him but I cry sometimes when I think about him, in my own solitude, in my own time, staring at the door, waiting.

I keep losing patience, which makes me angry. When I don't know what to do with all that anger, I burst into tears. I miss him so much and all I know is that I would rather have him back than have all these crayons and paints and drawing notebooks to play with. My favourite Barbie is the school Barbie even though she is not the prettiest. She is the only one I remember Papa playing with. I had a red toy car in which I would sit with my doll. I was the doll's driver and it was my job to send her to school. I would tell Papa to take us to school and he would push the car around the veranda. The car is still here, somewhere in the storehouse, gathering dust, its brakes rusting in the humidity of the storeroom. I try playing with it but Mummy is not home and Nani gets tired soon. I once tried playing with it in this new house and asked Bhaiyya to push it around. He seemed uninterested. Lifelessly, without a smile on his face or a spark in his eyes, he pushed the car around like it was his job. It was his job.

I had him put the car back in the storeroom. I will wait till Papa comes back.

ဟ

The doorbell rings. Every time the bell rings, I assume it's him. I get up fast on my tiny legs and run, my mind going back to the ten million things I have to say to him—the things I've thought about over and over again. This time I'm sure it is finally him. It has to be. I pray.

It's not.

It's Mummy, her face tired but her lips curled in a faint smile at the sight of me. Despite her long day at the office, she sits down to comfort me.

'You are my everything, my little sunshine, my little ladoo,' she says. I look up at her. Mummy and I, we never have to talk, we understand each other's silences. It's a secret language only we know.

'Do you remember Papa?' She asks as usual.

Of course I remember him.

10

Jalandhar, 1980

They didn't expect to come back to their grandparents' house like this. Raji and Pammi had plans to go back to the *pind* for the long summer vacation once they were done with the first semester at school. They would buy toys for their cousins and play with it the whole summer. It would've been so much fun, they thought. Because of frequent travelling, they didn't know their paternal family as well but now it seemed like it was all going to change. The moment the news was sent across to Punjab, the whole family came. They insisted the funeral be held back in the pind where all their family was, so they went back to Punjab with their grandfather, the four of them now a family of three.

All their lives they had wondered what their dad's parents' house looked like and now they saw. They lived in a village on the outskirts of the main city.

The house in the village that was theirs was nothing like the ones in Vizag or Nangal. There were no sea or mountains here, just acres and acres of farmland and a tube well to keep the lands irrigated. The house looked as though it was about to crumble any moment. The paint was chipping off the walls and the gaps in the bricks had become the home of ants and bees. It was not the biggest bungalow but it was enough for two small girls and their mother.

This was all they had, a worn-out house, an inheritance, an idea of a home and each other.

Amarjeet put her foot down and said that she wanted her daughters to study. She did not budge, she did not falter. If there was one thing she knew it was this—that both her daughters deserved the best education in the world, and she would fight the whole world if she had to to provide it for them. They were not only her daughters but their father's too, and he had had dreams for them. She was going to keep the promises she had made to make sure the girls had a good life.

They were both admitted to the best school in the city, St Joseph's Convent. It had been a long while since she had forgotten to feel anything but sadness, but the day she took her daughters for their interview, she felt pride and joy. The principal of the school could not stop gushing about the girls' interview and their previous grades and how proud she was to have them join the school. When she saw her daughters stand in the corridor of their new school, looking at the art on the boards as she spoke to the principal, her chest welled up with pride and her eyes moistened. Today was a victory. Their first victory.

From that day onwards, they both began to wake up at five every morning so that they could take the first bus to the city to reach the school before the assembly started. To anyone else, this would have been distressing—waking up early and taking a bus from the outskirts to reach school earlier than every other kid and coming back home late. But Raji and Pammi turned the early morning empty corridors of the school into their playground and the bus ride into an adventure.

The school belonged to them in a way it did not belong to anybody else. Every morning, they witnessed the building standing tall in isolation, waiting for the children to come and fill life in it, and they related to that sense of waiting. In their own way, they were waiting too, to feel alive again.

11

Gurmehar, Age Five
Jalandhar, 2001

It's the first day of school. This blue skirt, white top and red belt is all I have ever wanted. I twirl around in delight to see the skirt billow. Mummy went to the same school and so did Papa. Last night, I could not sleep due to sheer excitement. I kept arranging and rearranging my pencil box. I had two blue pencils and two pink pencils. I had three erasers, all in different shapes. There was a Winnie the Pooh eraser, a burger-shaped eraser and one normal eraser. I know I will not use the cartoon erasers since they make the paper black but I'm very happy to have them because they make my collection look nice. The pencil box has a sharpener attached to it which pops out when I click a small button but I still keep an extra one in hand.

We both wake up early. Mummy makes me Bournvita-milk in the morning as usual. We brush our teeth. I can't help giggling and bubbling the foam in my mouth. I am going to my favourite school. We met Noor's and Gargi's mothers when we went for admissions and then later at the book counter. Both of them will be there too and the thought makes me happy. Mummy finds the bubbling hilarious too, even though she keeps telling me not to do it.

'Gulgul, brush your teeth and stop doing this,' she says, trying to hold back her laughter.

She puts shampoo in my hair and then follows it up with conditioner, a routine she reserves for special occasions. 'Your hair will look super soft and nice,' she says, as she massages the shampoo in my head. I play with the foam and blow bubbles, a trick I recently learnt from my neighbour.

'Now you look perfect,' Mummy says, tucking my shirt in and smoothening the pleats of my skirt. I pick my bag up. I had to remember a few details by heart and Mummy quizzed me about it multiple times. There was always an extra pause before I took my father's name. Mummy taught me to go on and explain that he was no more and that he had died in war. I did not understand most of it. I was only repeating what everyone had been telling me for the longest time. These were just words that I mumbled without understanding the meaning.

We sit in Mummy's car. She recently learnt how to drive and these days we go out more often than before. 'Will you drop me every day?' I ask.

'Not every day. Mummy has to go to office. In the afternoon you will wait in front of the gate for your old buggy uncle to pick you up, you understand?' she asks as she fastens my seat belt. I hate wearing the seat belt; it makes my legs stick out while I sit stuck to the seat.

We have reached the school. It is full of people. The big iron gates are wide open and welcoming. I can't wait to go in, so I jump off the car and run, Mummy following me. I see Noor standing in the corner. I scream her name and run to hug her. I look around to find my other friends from nursery school. I see them holding their parents' hands. Their mummies are carrying their bags and their fathers are talking to each other. I stand there alone. I see my mother far away, walking towards me, in her cream-coloured suit and a boring bun unlike Noor's and Gargi's mothers who are wearing their prettiest suits for the occasion, the colour of their lipstick matching the hot pink of their outfits.

'Where are your parents?' a random uncle asks me as I wait with my bag hanging from my shoulders. Tears of embarrassment well up in my eyes. I am alone whereas everyone is here with both their parents. My mother did not even bother to dress up and I am carrying my own bag. Why do I have to be different? I realize I don't want to go to this school. My dreams shatter. I hate this place already. I hate everyone.

I run back to my mother and flap my hands at her. 'I want to go back. I hate you. Take me home now,' I cry. She doesn't understand.

'What happened, did someone say something?'

'Everyone's father came. Why hasn't my father come?'

Mummy's face becomes sombre. Her voice goes back to her usual strict tone, 'Go to class and don't say things like this. You will be fine.'

She hugs me and kisses my cheeks. She wipes away my tears and asks me to toughen up and be brave. Everyone around me finds this cute. They laugh and say that I am just scared of going to school. My mother pretends to agree with the parents, her voice croaking as she lies her way past all the questions.

She sends me to class and waves goodbye. I walk a few steps ahead and turn back to see her leave the gate.

She walks towards the water cooler at the far end of the ground. I wait and watch, tears dripping down my face. She looks around to confirm that no one is there and then collapses near the tap as she tries to wash her face.

An aunty pulls me back into the class and I sit down on a bench, my first day of school, trying to remember all the things I was supposed to say.

Father's occupation?

'Died in war, died in war, died in war,' I repeat the odd sentence to make sure I don't forget it.

12

Saharanpur, 1980s

A point came when it did not make sense. They were both growing up. Something had to be done. Soon their *dadaji*, their paternal grandfather, the head of the house, would refuse to let them travel in the bus alone. It was too risky to send two pubescent girls to the city on an empty bus every morning, especially during winter when the fog was dense. People would talk.

Amarjeet was smart and she had learnt how to work around everyone. She had started giving tuitions to the village children and turned a small room in the house into a tailor shop. This seemed like a harmless way of putting food on the table while staying within the security of the four walls of her own house, provided it did not offend the elders or disturb the 'culture' of the household. People were much kinder to them now that she was helping their kids pass their exams. Over time, she had also begun to develop something of a friendship with the women in the village. They would have long conversations while the women waited to get their suits stitched, altered or fixed. Small acts of kindness by people made survival a lot less difficult.

And yet, this was no way of living a life. There were no picnics, no clubs and definitely no 'ice cream evenings'. Sometimes, if she was feeling particularly happy, she would get a rasgulla or gulab jamun from the sweet shop in the village. This time, when Pammi and Raji fared well in their classes, there wasn't a rasgulla waiting for them. She knew they would have to be sent away to her brother's house if she wanted them to complete their education.

Despite the resistance from home, she finally convinced their grandfather to let her send them away to her brother's. It was a tough choice to make, but it was an important one. Both of them were put on a train and sent all the way to Uttar Pradesh.

They missed their mother terribly, but they were happy to be with their *mamaji* and his children. Amarjeet's brothers loved her and her two daughters very much. The girls were always more than welcome at their houses. The house in Saharanpur was the closest thing they could have to the house in Nangal. It was a huge house with a large backyard that was home to different trees: jamun, guava and orange. Most of their time was spent playing hide-and-seek or running around the house. There were five cousins in total, including Pammi and Raji. This was the kind of house they had wanted to be in all the time.

But in their hearts, they knew this was not permanent. They knew it was difficult for their uncle to take care of them all the time. No one ever said anything, but there were these backhanded compliments and taunts they had to listen to every now and then from their neighbours or distant relatives. While the boys were fed eggs and meat, they had to do with rotis without ghee and simple gravy. 'Girls don't eat meat or ghee. Ghee will make you fat,' their aunt would say as they both eyed their cousins' plates.

A beautiful sunny Sunday. For once, Raji did not have homework. The teachers were kind enough to let the students have a weekend without extra work after a particularly hard test they had to prepare for. Raji, unlike Pammi, was not one to sit idle. She wanted to go out and have fun.

The house was right next to the railway tracks. Their favourite game usually cost her a lot of money. Since she was the youngest of them all, they would bully her into giving them all her coins. They knew the names of almost all the trains that ran on those lines and they would play betting games. Whoever correctly guessed the train's name would win the coin flattened by the train. It had no value in the real world, but to a collector it was gold. There was a super car-flattened coin and then there was a *maal gaddi*-flattened coin. It was a competition.

Today, though, was not the day to play on the tracks. It was a Sunday and Sundays were special. The day started with getting up later than usual. There was some comfort in sleeping. It was a temporary escape from reality. She would often stay up longer than everyone else and cram everything that was in her books. There was only one way to get out of this place. Her father had been an officer and she wanted to become one too. She wanted to get her mother a bigger house and a better life.

Two days ago, her mother had sent them both parcels from home: one contained clothes and the other bottles of pickle. She took out a new white frock and wore it. It hung from her bony shoulders, but she couldn't stop looking in the mirror.

'Bhaiyya, let's go pluck fruits,' she told her eldest cousin.

'No, you go alone. I don't want to come,' he replied. He was too busy counting the bottle caps he had collected.

'I can't go alone, and I don't know how to climb trees. You come, *na*? You can climb the trees and I can collect the jamuns. There is salt in the kitchen and we can all have it.'

The idea was not so bad. He agreed.

He climbed up the tree and asked Raji to stand below to collect the fruit. She was quick as a fox in collecting the little pieces that fell and tied them in her frock. When she felt she couldn't fit any more, she asked him to come down.

The sun was hanging low in the sky. The birds chirped as they sat on the tree eating the fruit.

When Pammi and the rest of the gang arrived to join them, Raji teased: 'We beat you to it!'

'Yes, we have already taken all the ripe, low-hanging jamuns,' her partner in crime added.

'You have also managed to colour your white dress purple,' Pammi said. When Raji looked down, she realized that her brand new dress was completely stained.

But she grinned. These jamuns were great. The day was beautiful. Life was not as bad as it seemed on certain days and her stained frock would remind her of that.

ᔕ

No one knew what it was with this family. They did not know what they had done to deserve this fate over and over again. You think you know grief and you think you understand what pain feels like but even pain knows how to show its presence the moment you think you've numbed your senses.

One of their relatives, a boy their age with whom they had spent hours playing with, passed away all of a sudden. It must have been one of those days when they were all playing catch around the puddles in the park. There was nothing to be warned about. Every year, the monsoon would come and every year the rainwater would stand in the hollows of land. It was a new country, a young one, and no one complained about the puddles. Instead, they would float paper boats in them. There were paper boat races that the boy would invariably win. Who could have imagined that the same puddles were lying there breeding death?

For days, it was assumed that it was just a fever. A week passed and in a flash he was gone. The family thought they were doomed; it was the third young death in less than a decade.

It was the time when Amarjeet had come to stay with the kids. The three of them stayed reticent. They sensed what was going to come their way. They knew it. It was what it was and there was no point taking it to heart because it was grief talking.

The first time they heard it was when a neighbour was talking to a relative who had come to pay her respects.

'Who asked them to keep a widow and her daughters in their house? They bring bad luck. Look, now they are all cursed.' Raji stood behind a curtain and heard the whole thing.

That night, she went to her mother and told her what she had heard. 'Mummy, they said this happened because of us.'

'This' of course referred to the crowded house, the sadness in the air and the wails of women.

'We have survived so far, we will survive this too,' Amarjeet tried to comfort her daughter but how do you comfort a child whose tiny body has borne the brunt of so many tragedies?

∽

The whole day people kept pouring in and pouring out. Their eyes stung from the overflow of tears and the complete lack of it at the same time. They had nothing to do. Yet, the day left them exhausted, drenched in sorrow.

It had been a long day. The body was sent for cremation and other ceremonial rites. The women stayed back to clean up. As per custom, the kitchen was closed and no food was to be cooked till they were done with all the prayers.

His mother turned to Amarjeet. 'Will this ever go?' She was referring to the feeling that felt like pain but was so much worse. Pain eventually passes, but loss is something that stays with you every single day of your life. It haunts you during moments of silence, during the empty days. It becomes your identity because it never leaves your eyes, no matter how loudly you laugh. It forms a barricade between your smile and your eyes.

That night, the house was cleaned and all the mattresses were turned into makeshift beds. The elders of the house slept in the bedrooms and everybody else had to manage with the mattresses in the hall. Raji was so tiny she simply curled up by her mother in the mattress put against the wall. The air was thick with humidity and the borrowed table fans did nothing to make the heat any better.

Pammi, though, could not find a mattress or even a sheet. 'Aunty, where are the mattresses?' Pammi asked one of the women sitting in the group. The conversation came to an abrupt, uncomfortable halt.

The woman calmly directed her to a mattress in a corner of the hallway. 'Use that.'

Pammi gasped. 'Aunty, but this is . . . where he was!'

'So? You're lucky I'm even giving you something to sleep on!'

It was the same mattress on which the young boy's lifeless body lay not more than five hours ago. Pammi walked out of the room with the mattress hugged close to her chest. She could still smell the marigolds, camphor and the faint smell of flesh. Tears dripped down her face, but she made no noise. She dropped the mattress the moment the hall door shut behind her. Her knees were too weak for her to stand—she fell on the same mattress and burst into sobs. She missed her brother. She sobbed and cursed the day he got bit by the mosquito. She sobbed for her father. She sobbed because she knew she had no home and because she had never felt this alone.

∽

A few weeks later, they moved back to Punjab.

13

Gurmehar, Age Three
Pathankot, 1999

We have come to Papa's unit today—me, Mummy, Dadu, Bani and Maasi. I'm beginning to make sense of things. There is something about cantonments, the crisp air, the discipline, the cleanliness, the properly maintained roads, the people in uniforms. I feel safe here, almost victorious, though I have no idea what quest it is that I'm a part of. I'm slightly closer to winning whenever I'm here. This place reminds me of him.

Even the leaves don't move here without permission and I remember Papa. No one would do anything without his permission, not even me. I think about him a lot but it's only natural because everyone around me is talking about him in hushed, sad voices. I giggle whenever I remember something particularly funny. This is how I amuse myself. I have been going to a lot of places with Mummy where I need to keep myself entertained: government offices, cantonment offices, gurdwaras, functions. When relatives come, they make it a point to see me and give me hugs, however strange and forced their hugs might be. The aunties insist I sit on their laps as they run their hands through my hair, planting kisses on my forehead. It is a different aunty every time but it's the same conversation. I have learnt how to block it. I play with the hem of my frock and my hair, suck my thumbs and look around. Today we've come to Papa's unit. Mummy tells me they are going to honour Papa and that there will be a ceremony. I get scared at the word 'ceremony' because the last time there was one there were gun salutes which were very loud, so loud that they still echo in my head. I ask Mummy if there will be guns, she tells me she isn't sure. I wonder if she is as scared of guns as I am.

'Are you scared of guns, Mummy?' I ask her while we are still in the car. I enjoy car rides, they're calm and quiet and no one is there to bother us. I sit on her lap, tuck my head in the nook of her neck and breathe into the familiarity, a rare bit of it, whatever semblance of normalcy is left. I take her dupatta and put it over my head and everything is gone. The real world stops existing and my whole world shrinks itself into the tent of her dupatta; it is my temporary home. Some days my world is light green, some days it is yellow. It used to have sequins and stars and lace once upon a time, and on those days my world would be a rainbow, the sun passing through my prism of safety. The colourful dupattas have gone, replaced by plain beige, white and occasionally pale yellow, and with that is gone my colourful world.

'I'm not scared and you shouldn't be either. We cannot be scared any more,' she tells me as I lift my face out from the dupatta to look at her looking at me, her brown eyes tired.

'I won't,' I promise her and go back to my own world where I don't have to be scared.

People always tell me that my dad was very brave, Mummy is his brave wife and we are his brave daughters, and I'm beginning to believe that. The meaning of the word 'brave' was unclear to me before but now I think I have a better idea. It means without fear, it means strong and it means someone who will do whatever it takes. The only thing is the context. I want to be brave like my dad. I've always wanted to be like him. When I told Mummy this last time she laughed and said it was unusual. Girls usually want to be like their mothers, but here I was telling her I wanted to be like Papa. I really want to know whom Bani would want to be like. I want to ask her but she doesn't talk. She has eyes like buttons that she moves around here and there when I go and play with her.

Bani plays with a lot of my toys. I get really mad at this as I don't want to share my toys with her. She doesn't even know how to play with them. She just takes a toy and shakes it in the air and does something with her face. It looks as if she is laughing though she doesn't laugh a lot, barely actually. She cries all the time and sleeps the rest. I've complained to Mummy that I don't want to give her my toys because she throws them and they break. I suggest she buys her new ones to call her own. Mummy says once things are better she will get us both our own things and promises that we won't ever have less of anything. She tells me she will buy Bani and me thousands of toys but for now I will have to adjust. The situation at home, she tells me, isn't favourable, like bad weather for driving. She talks to me in a language whose words I understand but meaning I don't. I think when I grow older like our new neighbour I will. When I become ten years old, I will become strong and I will understand the meaning of everything. Bani will say she wants to be like Mummy, I think. She doesn't know who Papa is. But if he comes back then maybe she would want to be like him too. Who wouldn't?

My dad used to drink this bitter drink called rum from huge glass bottles. It was such a long, lavish process. There was something very special about it, almost as if time had paused and everything was at rest. There would be two bowls of *namkeen* set on the tray along with the golden magical liquid in a short glass. What made it even more magical was the fact that it was forbidden.

I remember asking him one day what he was drinking. He laughed and said this was *kodi dawai*, bitter medicine.

'What do you need medicine for?' I asked.

He said it was to forget the things he had seen.

'What things have you seen?'

'The ones in my office.'

'Valley?' I asked. I knew he went to the Valley—that was his office.

'You are such a talkative child! Come here,' he said and lifted me in the air and tickled me till I lost my breath from laughing. He was stronger than Mummy, so it was fun playing aeroplane with him. He would turn me into an aeroplane and whirl me around in circles. It would make me laugh a lot. I haven't laughed like that in a very long time.

We have reached the unit and we are waiting in the mess. I see the same bottle of kodi dawai on the shelves here.

One day, when we used to live in Nani's house and Papa was home for a break, I saw a cracked bottle of the dawai lying in the veranda. He wasn't home and I thought why not have a sip of whatever was left. The moment the liquid touched my tongue Papa came. I dropped the bottle and started crying. I knew I would be in trouble. The dawai was so bad it burnt my tongue. Papa had seen me. Only Mummy could save me now.

I yelled, 'Mummy, look what Papa did, he gave me kodi dawai!'

Mummy came out to the veranda. She looked at Papa who stood at the main door of the house and started laughing. There was something extremely funny in my little antic and my burnt tongue. This made me cry more. They were both laughing at me. To pacify me, the three of us later went to get Frooti.

The bottle on the mess shelf reminds me of that. It reminds me of him and of everything my life was not any more since he is not here. I miss the giggle that left my mother's mouth and I miss the ease with which she breathed. She isn't the same any more. I look at her sitting here. She sits stiffer than usual; her smile, though polite, is clearly fake, it doesn't reach her eyes. Everyone in the room is kind and courteous enough not to point it out or maybe they do not want to acknowledge it. I just want to go back to my little world, so I take the corner of her dupatta and put it over my head.

After the ceremony I notice something I had seen before. A round flower piece—they call it a wreath. It was at the foot of the box that Papa was last seen in. He was behind these flowers.

Is he still behind these flowers?

I walk around the memorial and pick the wreath up and look for him.

Just a plain wall.

Not him.

14

Jalandhar, 1980s

Young Harry with his two younger brothers were studying in a convent boys' school when the Khalistan movement in Punjab gained mass support and slowly turned violent. A concern that originated from the fear of alienation during Partition grew on to become one of the largest religious separatist movements in India, leading to years of terrorism and fear in Punjab.

Harry was in class X when he first understood the revolutionary Bhagat Singh. He remembered reading about him in his class VI history textbook but it was only when the school organized an Independence Day skit that he really began to develop an interest in this boy who was not much older than he was and had given up his life for the nation.

Being the tall, handsome, sardar boy in his class it was only natural that he was selected to play Bhagat Singh. The role wasn't much, it was a school production with an almost negligible budget and a strict time limit where they had to accommodate three speeches, four dance performances and pull out one raffle draw winner from each class. Their characters only had one dialogue each and a few stunts where they had to pretend to attack a train with fake guns in their hands as the voice-over narrated the story.

The first time Harry delivered his only dialogue, he could feel the adrenaline surge in his body. He stood on the stage with a fake noose hanging in front of his face and said, '*Sarfaroshi ki tamanna ab hamare dil mein hai, dekhna hai zor kitna bazue katil mein hai. Inquilab zindabad!*' His heartbeat quickened and his pupils dilated. At that moment he would have done anything for the country and its people. Maybe it was the young blood or maybe it was that he was a great actor who could really get into his character but at that moment he knew he wanted to learn more about this revolutionary he was playing. He was only a few years younger than Bhagat Singh—who had given up his life for the freedom of his people. Harry felt there was definitely more that he should be able to do. That evening he went to his father and asked him to tell him more about Bhagat Singh.

'Which gun did Bhagat Singh have?' he asked his dad, a tall turbaned gentleman who knew all about guns, ammunition, motors and agriculture. His father was a deeply religious man who knew each and every *shabad* by heart and read from the Gurbani every day. While he was extremely religious he was an equally liberal man. Religion should let you grow as human beings and evolve with time to stay relevant, he taught his sons. In their family, it was their mother who went to work, a rare thing for women to do in small towns such as Jalandhar.

'I don't know which gun he had but I think it was either a crude gun that was made in the black market or a smooth piece of machinery that he stole from the British. It's tough to say which one,' he told his son whose eyes shone at the talk of guns.

'Papa, will you show me a gun? I really want to know what it feels like to hold one. I'm playing Bhagat Singh in the Independence Day skit and I think it would really help me.'

'First *puttar ji*, you have to pass my test.'

'What test?'

'The test to know if you are responsible enough or not. Now tell me, if you had a gun what would you use it for?'

The answer to this question was simple, he didn't need to think about it twice. 'I would use it to help people and to fight for India, to be a change-maker—a revolutionary like Bhagat Singh.'

'Would you use it to scare people and make them do work for you?'

Harry thought about it. Is that what revolutionaries do? 'No, I will use it to fight the enemy and to protect people like Bhagat Singh.'

His father went to his room, took a dummy revolver that they had kept in case of emergency, and then went on to explain the functioning of it to his curious son. 'It's better that I teach him before someone else does,' he thought to himself. These were tough times.

There was nothing that Harry wanted more at that point. His heart craved to do something, anything that would bring impact. He wanted to save people, he wanted to free people. He wanted to fight for them.

The next day, during the Independence Day skit, though he did not have a real revolver, he had a toy gun that fit just right in his young, bony hands. If that little object and a heart full of passion were enough for Bhagat Singh to fight for the country, then it should be enough for him too. The conviction in his dialogue was real, the fire in his eyes was one that would not be put out.

15

Gurmehar, Age Six
Jalandhar Cantonment, 2002

In Papa's trunk was a collection of daggers that he wanted to frame and hang on the wall. It was one of his passions, the weapons, he liked to collect them. In our living room there is a special wall with a shelf dedicated to his collections of empty bullet shells, swords and medals. Many of our Sundays are spent with a bottle of Brasso and rolls of cottons by our side to make sure his collection never loses its shine. It becomes a competition between Mummy and me to see whose bullet shell shines more. I keep polishing it till I can see my reflection staring back at my six-year-old face in this weapon of destruction.

People often ask me about the things I want to do when I grow up. I have thought long and hard about it. My only dream is to be like my father, to be the same person that he was and to emulate his personality. Would it comfort my mother to see me walking around the house giggling and happy, to see his shadow, a watered down version of him, alive? I think it would.

Often I try to create an image of my father in my head from whatever people have told me in bits and pieces. I sit on the same chair as him and use his favourite mug. The other day Mummy bought us fancy milk sippers with Disney cartoons on them but I refused to drink from it. It doesn't taste the same, it doesn't feel the same. When I grow up I want to be like my father—brave, giving, patriotic and kind. Everybody talks about Papa's bravery in long monologues, telling me his stories whenever we meet. I'm surrounded by very kind people; uncles from his unit never shy away from talking about him. In fact they *want* to talk about him, they want to remember him, and I like to sit and listen, and it almost feels like he is right there, listening to us. I don't need superheroes to believe in. I don't need stories of far-off galaxies and fictional victories of good over evil to keep me entertained or put me to sleep. I have my father, my superhero, my favourite story.

Jasmine is my best friend who lives right opposite our house in a small housing society of the cantonment. But this is not the only house that I have. I have Dadi's house, Nani's house and Mummy's house, which is being constructed. We go to the building site frequently and those are the few times Mummy carries me in her arms. We walk through the foundations of the new house as she tells me about her vision of the life she was building, brick by brick.

The house will have a huge kitchen with open windows and a dining room right next to it with a nook for a tall fridge unlike our smaller one now. 'We will have five rooms in the house, one for each of us, and an extra one for the friends you want to invite. There will be a huge wall with your papa's pictures and trophies and on the same wall, when you grow up, I will keep yours. The bathrooms will have showers, a massive bathtub and a place to hang your fluffy towels on. And when you come out of the shower looking like a princess you will step into a cupboard full of clothes to wear—you will never not have anything.' She says this in my ear as she carries me through the house.

Jasmine and I have a fight. I pull her ponytail and scratch her face. We are pulled apart by Jasmine's mom. I am so angry. I think about bravery and about Papa. I think about power and about being strong. Strong people hit harder and win and in that moment I decide to go home and get one of the daggers.

Bhaiyya sees the dagger in my hand and takes it. He takes my tiny hand in his other hand and walks me to my mother, telling her of my teary face, the fight and the sudden appearance of the weapon.

'What were you thinking?' Mummy asks me, her voice dripping with anger. I am shivering. I have never seen her like that.

I tell her about my fight with Jasmine and about wanting to be brave like Papa.

'That is not how friendships work and that is not how you win people. You can't win with authority or dictatorship. You don't want to be feared; you want to be loved and being loved is so much more a happier feeling than fear.'

That day I learnt one of the most important lessons of my life: my father's weapons may have been guns and ammunition, but my weapon had to be peace. Always.

16

Jalandhar, 1988

On the last day of college, they had a practical exam. It was a breezy afternoon as Raji and her friend walked out of their classrooms with a new sense of freedom and weightlessness. There did lie a future that had to be taken care of, there were discussions to be made, but today was to be spent rejoicing the last day of college. There were no more examinations to cram for and no more ink on hands. A world full of opportunities lay in front of all of them. Raji took a deep, happy breath. Her mother and sister waited at home, probably preparing her favourite food. That's what they did when Pammi came back after her last exam. Pammi gave Raji hope—they were a family of fighters making their own way in the world. Her sister was pursuing her masters and she knew now it was her turn to study. Biology was her favourite subject and while she really looked forward to studying more of it, she let that thought pass and focused just on the food, a night of chatty conversations and easy sleep that lay ahead of her. Her eyes were tired from not having slept the previous night as she ploughed through her books, one after the other.

'Here, this is for you,' her friend said as she handed her an envelope. Raji eyed it with suspicion. As she turned it over, she saw whom it was from. They had never spoken to each other in the three years they had spent together in college but somehow the little cream envelope did not come as a surprise.

She opened it carefully and took out a folded piece of paper. It was a letter. She wrapped her fingers tightly around it as she walked towards the end of the corridor to read it in a quiet space. Her friend kept asking her about the contents of the letter but she wouldn't show it to her. Her eyes ran over every word once again and her lips curled into a tiny smile.

In the letter, which was later taken home and kept securely in a tiny box, Harry requested if they could talk and be friends. It was the last day of college, after all, and they might never speak to each other ever again.

'We will both move on with our lives, you will go your way and I will go mine, but I hope we stay friends and remain in touch. I'm not a bad person whom you may not want to talk to. I will prove to be a good person. I understand that in our country it is very difficult for people of two genders to be friends with each other but I promise you that I'm a nice person. Please think about it and don't make a decision at the toss of a coin,' read the letter, written by twenty-year-old Harry in a neat handwriting on a clear sheet of paper. It was signed off with his signature and a smile.

Raji was a quiet, shy girl who kept her nose buried in either course books or an occasional magazine. Like every nineteen-year-old, she would swoon over movie actors and film stories but never in her life had she expected a letter to be delivered to her in such a filmy style. 'I can go talk to him; there is no harm in talking. Plus the letter is so thoughtfully written,' she thought.

She and her friend walked over to the administration block, a part of the old structure of the college that was always properly maintained, with the grass nicely trimmed, with the flowers in the flowerpots in perfect bloom and the walls painted evenly.

'Hello,' she said quietly, smiling ear to ear.

'Hello, I'm Mandeep Singh,' he said.

It was the first time in three years that she had found out that his name was Mandeep. All these years she had referred to him as Harry because everyone around her did so. The three spoke for a while, laughing and giggling, discussing the paper and where they were from. It seemed like the conversation would never end. After all, they had three years of conversation to catch up on.

The more they talked the more they realized how similar they were. Raji had always thought of him as the boy on an Enfield. She knew him as the bodybuilder who had won competitions. But this was the first time she had actually spoken to him. He was sweet, kind and surprisingly shy. Every word he said was said with purpose. He would not say anything that was unnecessary. There were boys in college who believed in showing off, who were self-centred and always talked over women, but not him; he let her speak, listening intently, saying only as much as was needed. They realized they were neighbours and that their families knew each other's relatives.

'What are you going to do after college?' she asked, curious.

'I have taken entrance exams for law,' he told her.

'I will study more too. I have applied for BEd,' she said.

Suddenly, he said, 'I want to be in the army.' Where had this come from? He had never even admitted this to himself, but here he was, pouring his secret ambitions out to this beautiful girl.

They said their goodbyes to each other that day but their conversations never stopped.

17

Gurmehar, Age Two
En route to McLeodganj, April 1999

My eyes are following the trees. It is the first time I'm sitting in the back seat of the car. Papa is driving and Mummy is sitting in the front with baby Bani on her lap. I'm an elder sister now. I have to behave like one, many people have been telling me this. So this morning when we were ready to leave, I quietly went and sat in the back seat like a responsible elder sister. I felt so happy about it then but I don't feel too good now. It is so lonely in the back. Papa calls to check on me every fifteen minutes and I reply. We are going to the hills for a vacation, the whole family. I'm very excited because Papa promised there will be toys waiting for me when we get there. I do not want to spoil anybody's trip but my head is going round and round with the trees and now I can feel it in my stomach too.

It all comes out, the food we had before starting the trip, and is all over my sweater. I sit still. I'm scared Papa will scold me for spoiling my dress. Tears are welling up in my eyes. I have to stay quiet, I keep reminding myself.

'Gulgul,' Papa calls, his voice strong.

'Yes, Papa,' I say.

'Are you all right, beta? Everything good?'

'Yes, Papa.' I pray he doesn't find out and at the same moment he turns to look at me. His face loses its smile the moment he sees me. I know there is a scolding coming. Papa has never scolded me but I'm still very scared. I don't ever want to disappoint him but today I have.

'Raji, look what your daughter did,' he tells Mom as he pulls over to the nearby dhaba.

There is silence as Mom turns to look at me and then she looks at him. Their eyes meet and they both start laughing.

'Why didn't you tell us?' Mummy asks as she gets down from the car and opens my car door, the baby still sleeping in her arms. She looks at me with kind eyes and I know it is okay. Papa walks over to her from the other side.

'You leave it. I will take care of my baby,' he says. He comes and lifts me from the seat and kisses my forehead. 'Gulgul, you should have told us that you are not feeling well,' he says. He opens the trunk of the car to pull out a fresh pair of clothes for me. Papa looks at everything we have brought and chooses an orange sweater with denim dungarees. We go to the dhaba where he cleans my face and changes my clothes. Mummy and Bani wait in the car. 'Now look at you, so beautiful, the most beautiful girl in the world,' he tells me, softy tugging my ponytails.

I eye the Fanta bottle over his shoulder as he gets a plastic bag to put my clothes in. I don't know how to ask him. I gather courage. I tap on his back. 'Papa, Fanta,' I say meekly, trying my luck. He never lets me have anything unhealthy, especially not these drinks. I wait for the no.

It doesn't come. Instead, he asks the shopkeeper to open the dusty glass bottle and pour some of the fizzy orange liquid into a glass. He puts me on the ground and bends down to give me the drink. He holds the glass in one hand

and a napkin on the other, wiping my mouth after every sip I take.

As we walk back to the car, he asks me to promise him that I will tell him about anything that makes me uncomfortable without thinking twice. 'Your papa is here to fix everything,' he says.

We make our promises.

18

Jalandhar, 1992

The results of Harry's entrance exams came—he had cleared all his exams and had to leave for the officers' training academy in Chennai soon. Everyone at home was extremely excited and proud of him. The good news came on the day of Pammi's mehendi ceremony. It had been four years since Harry and Raji graduated and last year, with their families meeting each other, they had also got engaged. Sometimes it felt like a dream to them, how easily they had moved from not talking to being friends and now being engaged.

It seemed like a fairy tale. And now he was going to join the armed forces.

Amarjeet's heart soared with pride when Harry's mother told her the happy news over lunch. Amarjeet said a silent prayer in her heart as she took in her surroundings. Her house was beautifully decorated with lights and strings of marigolds. There were happy guests cheerfully talking and young kids dancing to the music playing in the background. Her elder daughter had completed her education and was now getting married into a lovely family from Mumbai. And then there was Harry, whom, since she had first met him, she had grown to be very fond of and now deeply loved. Harry's mother was a highly educated, incredible woman who was the principal of a local school. Between both the women, there was love and immense respect. They had both lived their lives on their own terms and had raised wonderful children. Harry had two younger brothers, Anu and Manu, whom Pammi and Raji loved like their own brothers.

∽

Anu, Manu and Raji sat in Harry's room with all his new uniforms. Pammi was downstairs with his mother learning a kadhi recipe. The acceptance letter had come along with information about the academy rules. He was supposed to have all his clothes marked with his initials so that he wouldn't lose them. Raji carefully took each and every piece of clothing and stitched 'HR' on it. She knew it would be difficult but they had promised to write each other letters and talk on the phone whenever they could.

'Don't worry, you will see me when I come back as an officer. I'll no longer be a small-town lad. I'll be in a uniform with stars on my shoulders,' he said, trying to console her.

'I will write to you,' she said and handed him an envelope full of stamps. 'I'm giving these to you just in case you don't find stamps there in your hostel.'

When Harry left, he seemed to take a part of her heart with him.

19

Jalandhar, 24 September 1996

Raji was being wheeled into the operation theatre of the military hospital on a stretcher, her mind losing track of what was happening. She could sense the light dim as the morphine kicked in. In a few hours she would be meeting the little human she had been longing to see. The last thing she remembered seeing was the tall shadow of man pacing along, breathless with nervousness, murmuring things in an attempt to comfort her.

ᔕ

Her eyes adjusted to the bright light of the hospital room as she slowly opened them. She felt like she had woken up from a deep sleep. Harry was there, looking at her expectantly, his heart full of love, eyes soft and kind. He was smiling, he couldn't wait to tell her the news. The words he had waited to say for the longest time poured out when he saw that she was awake: 'I'm the proud father of a baby girl,' he said, grinning ear to ear.

'Baby girl.'

The words echoed in her ears till she could finally understand them. She was in the hospital and had just regained consciousness after a complex Caesarian surgery. Her baby was born two months before the expected date. As the thoughts came back to her, her heart raced, unable to keep up.

'Baby girl?' she whispered back, confirming if she had heard correctly.

Harry, who was leaning against the wall, his arms crossed, smiled at her and nodded his head. A smile spread across Raji's face and her heart filled with love she had never felt before. How long had she been waiting to meet this miracle! They had prayed at every shrine in the country, every mandir, dargah and gurdwara, for their wish to come true.

The room, painted white, looked even brighter with the tube light flickering in the corner. The chilly September wind passing through its wide open windows made Raji uncomfortable—her body, now weak, felt colder than usual.

'I'm feeling cold,' she told Harry, whose smile didn't vanish for one single second. He quickly went and closed the window and pulled a blanket out of the care kit they had kept ready at home in anticipation of this day. She doubted if the bag had all the things she wanted, especially now that the baby had arrived early. She wondered what other surprise the baby would bring in the future. Her heart swelled with happiness at the thought of it.

As he pulled the blanket over his wife, he told her he had gone to the nursery to see the baby. 'She is a very tiny girl. The doctors won't let anyone meet her. They only let me in because I'm the father. They are saying she will need more time to heal and be stronger. But she is my daughter, I'm sure she will get better sooner than most kids. They've kept her in the incubator. Once you are fine, you can go see her,' he said, excitedly. He was already thinking of the future when his baby would be fitter and stronger, running around the house.

'I will never let anyone hurt her. I will never, ever leave her alone,' he thought, making promises in his head as he pictured the tiny being he had just seen with tubes and wires in the incubator.

'What does she look like?' came Raji's next question. She wanted to know what the baby looked like.

'She is . . .' Harry looked for the perfect words; how do you explain to someone what a miracle looks like? He blurted, 'Pink!'

'Pink?'

'She is small, the tiniest, most precious little baby, and her complexion is pink,' he told her, trying to paint a picture of their child in her head, hoping Raji could imagine her the exact way he saw her.

Raji was visited by many relatives that day, one after the other. Every one of them who came from the nursery told her bits and pieces about the baby she was yet to see.

'She is small.'

'Her head is full of curly hair.'

'The baby is very cute.'

'She needs to be fed a good diet as she grows up.'

'Our uncle's cousin's daughter's friend also had a Caesarian delivery. You will have to take a lot of care.'

She couldn't wait any longer. It had been five days of people coming in and telling her what her daughter looked like. She felt stronger now, her stitches were beginning to heal. The doctor came in early that morning and checked the readings on the machines as per schedule.

'Okay, let's take you to your kid,' he said, signalling to the nurse to get her a wheelchair. Raji's heart raced inside her chest. Just the thought of the baby made her eyes wet. She rested her hands on her lap, her fingers crossed, praying for her child's health. She hadn't even seen her and yet she knew that she would do anything in the world to keep her safe and protected, to provide for her and to turn her into a strong, independent, loving woman like her own mother.

The nursery was painted in pale yellow. She entered the room hoping she would see her child immediately but was welcomed by a sea of cribs and babies.

'I will look for my own baby,' she said. She was confident she would be able to find her own daughter. She had imagined her face so many times over the last few days.

She went to the first baby, the fattest, cutest child, confident that this would be her. The baby lay in the crib wrapped in soft white blankets, its cheeks squished against the mattress. It slept without a care in the world. She lifted the name tag at the end of the crib. It said 'Subedar Mann Singh'. This wasn't her baby. Like this, she went peeking into every crib, one after another, to look for the face she was sure she would find familiar.

Her baby was in the corner of the room, in the farthest crib, closer to the machines. 'That is the only one left,' she thought. Kindly, she asked the nurse to push her wheelchair towards it. It had to be her. She couldn't wait to meet her. All the dreams she had had of her came back to her. Her *own* baby. She lifted herself from the wheelchair slightly to have a look. In the corner of the crib, wrapped in a white blanket, was the tiniest baby in the whole world, so tiny that if one didn't look closely, they would assume that it was just a pile of blankets. The baby's face was blue, red and green, all at the same time. The machines were still attached to her tiny wrist which was the size of Raji's finger.

'Can I hold the baby?' Raji asked, unable to take it all in, her heart full of love, her eyes moist with tears and a sense of protectiveness in her mind she had never felt before.

She held the child, born after two years of marriage after so many prayers. She was so fragile. Her hand was wrapped tightly around her mother's finger. 'She will be the most loved child in this whole world. We will give her everything she wants. We will shower her with love and care. I will protect her with all my heart,' she kept thinking, over and over again. 'She is God's special child, his blessing, *Gurmehar*.'

'Isn't she the most beautiful girl in the world?' asked Harry from over her shoulder as he walked in to meet the two of them—his own family. Raji giggled. The baby was the different colours of the rainbow. She was also extremely weak, unlike the chubby, pink-cheeked babies she had seen earlier.

But yes. She was the most beautiful girl in the world.

20

Gurmehar, Age Fifteen
Boarding School, Ludhiana, 2011

The truth is, I don't want to live any more. My eyes are swollen to slits and I can barely see. My head is throbbing but I can't find the voice or the energy to walk to the infirmary to get any medicine. How will I face my coaches tomorrow? I have lost another match. Match after match. There is not one that I have won and today was the worst. I lost to a girl who was Bani's age.

I leave no stone unturned. No one goes on extra runs like I do and yet I lose matches and I'm the one with a bad ranking and bad tournaments.

I pick the handkerchief and blow my nose into it. Still in my match clothes, drenched in sweat, I sit on the bathroom floor, contemplating where to go from here. The sweat has now evaporated from my clothes, leaving a residue of salt. My muscles are throbbing, my legs are unable to lift me up.

It was a very long match, 4–6, 5–7. I tried, and yet here I am. I don't want to live any more. I have only ever loved one thing in my life and I'm horrible at it. How will I live life without tennis? I'm clearly not good enough. I will have to stop playing if I don't start playing internationally by eighteen. At fifteen, girls play junior grand slams and here I'm losing in a practice match. I don't want to live a life without tennis. I will kill myself—I will slit my wrists or I will jump off the building. There is nothing left to live for.

There is a knock on the bathroom door. It's Bani.

'Gul, Mummy is on the phone. Your coach called her as he saw you crying after the match. She wants to talk to you,' she says.

'I don't want to see anyone. Please go away,' I manage to say in the middle of my sobs.

'Listen, please talk to her, she is worried. She is calling on your phone now. Please take her call,' she begs me. I understand. I'm totally ruining poor Bani's win. She won her match. It makes me feel worse.

I check my phone. There are twenty-five missed calls from my mother. The sight of it scares me. I will have to talk to her. The phone lights up again, and it's her. I gather courage and pick it up.

'Hello,' I say, the word barely a whisper.

'Hello, beta?' Her voice sounds concerned. It makes me cry even harder. I miss Mummy so much, I want to go back home and not live here. I cannot hold my sobs in. 'Don't cry. Tell me what happened. It's just a match, Gul, don't cry. It's only a little match.' Her voice is soothing. 'Strong girls don't cry like this. Work harder this week and you will win the next time. Stop crying and talk to me.'

I can't talk. I don't know what to say. I just tell her the truth. 'I'm so bad at it. I want to die. I hate this life. I don't want to be a loser at the thing that I love the most,' I weep to her over the phone.

'Beta, you are such a hard worker. No one works harder than you. It is not about winning; it's about your character and you are not losing there.'

'I don't want to live!' This is all I can manage to say. My throat is now sore.

'I live, na?' she asks quietly. 'I'm also living a life where I've lost the thing I loved the most. Look at me surviving, living and doing well for all of us. Will you give up life or tennis just as easily? Did I ever give up? I was only twenty-eight when I lost your father. I wanted to give up then too. What did I do?'

My mother never gave up. She worked day and night and built a house for us. She provided us comforts beyond what was required. She was strong and ambitious and, despite everyone suggesting otherwise, let both of us pursue sports even when it came in the way of traditional education. She lived—lives—life on her own terms.

'Life is a fight. It is a war in itself. Nothing is ever going to be fair. It was never fair for me, it was never fair for Nani and today it won't be fair for you, but we are not women who give up. We get up and we keep going. You're the daughter of a martyr. Your father fought in the forest hills and you are scared of crackers on Diwali? He lived amongst the deadliest ammunition. He took the bullet in his heart for the nation, that's how brave he was. It is this blood that runs in your veins. He was a man who never quit. And you say you will quit at life?' she says with more authority. I love it when she switches from comforting to scolding in the same breath. This is typical Mummy. I smile in spite of myself.

'It doesn't matter how good you are. Work hard and you will get better. In the next match, you will win. You are not a diamond, you are not the most precious stone in the world, and I don't want you to believe that you are. You are a slab of iron ore. You will go through the furnace and you will come out strong, like iron. Life will throw rocks at you and beat you with hammers but you will take those beatings in your stride and come out like a sword, a weapon. Make your weaknesses your strength. Cry it out today, but tomorrow be prepared to go through the motions all over again. This is life for you. You win, you lose, but you do not give up.'

'Yes, Mummy,' I say.

Fall down seven, get up eight.

he was. It was the blood [illegible]

[illegible] And [illegible]

[illegible]

[illegible]

[illegible]

[illegible]

It [illegible] of how good [illegible] Work

[illegible] will get [illegible]

[illegible] not [illegible] you are not

the [illegible] world, and [illegible]

[illegible] if you are [illegible]

[illegible] You will go [illegible]

[illegible]

[illegible]

[illegible]

[illegible]

[illegible]

[illegible]

[illegible]

[illegible]

[illegible]

[illegible]

21

Jodhpur, 1997

When Harry was transferred to Jodhpur, Raji moved with him, taking with her their three-month-old daughter. She also carried with her all her interior decoration magazines. Her head was full of ideas and she was ecstatic. She thought the new house would provide her with a canvas to try her interior decoration skills. She looked forward to their life together now with a daughter to complete their family.

It was the first time they had gone back to their unit since the baby's birth. The whole unit, which was Harry's extended family, welcomed them with open arms. It had become routine for them to host dinners in their house whenever someone wanted to come see the baby. The women's club was especially kind to Raji, giving her tips on how to raise the baby, what food babies love best and what medicines would come in handy. They would meet in the evenings for walks when Raji brought the baby in a red pram covered with mosquito net.

Independence Day was around the corner. Three young officers along with Harry decided to do something special to celebrate it that year. They wanted to do something unusual, something more than the regular party or dinner. Mehrangarh Fort had an annual Independence Day celebration on the evening of 14 August that went on through the night and ended with a huge fireworks show at midnight. They decided that they would go for the celebrations.

Dressed in jackets and shirts, they left for the fort on their bikes. Harry rode on his Royal Enfield with his whole family, Raji and three-month-old Gulgul. They had spent the whole day wondering if they should take the baby along, but he could not imagine his little girl not being by his side. Independence Day evoked deep emotions in him. Every year on this day, he would become the same fourteen-year-old boy who once played the part of Bhagat Singh in a play, and his heart would fill with pride for the nation. He couldn't wait for his daughter to grow up. He wanted to tell her stories of heroes, he wanted to know how she felt about them, he wanted her to know that she was free in this country and that these were the people who were responsible for that freedom. With these hopes, they took the baby with them.

It was a sight to behold, the clear sky from the height of the fort. The fort itself was decorated with orange and yellow flowers. The artillery gun was decorated with candles and lights. The fireworks were meant to be shot into the sky from there.

When the clock struck twelve, the sky turned into a canvas for fireworks. People were standing on the edge of the fort, taking in the grandeur.

A woman saw them watching the fireworks from afar and ran towards them. She seemed unusually excited to see them. 'Ma'am, I'm from the *Patrika*!' she said, tapping Raji's arm. Raji looked at her, startled.

'Excuse me?' she asked politely.

'I'm sorry. I mean I'm from *Rajasthan Patrika*, the newspaper,' she said.

'Of course,' Raji said. She waited for her to say more, her eyes darting towards Harry, wondering what a reporter would want from them.

'I just wanted to know how you managed to get such a small baby here at this hour? What's her name? She is so cute,' she said and took out a notepad and pen from her handbag.

Raji told her their baby's name and why they were there.

The next morning's local newspaper read, 'Months-old Gulgul at Mehrangarh Fort, celebrating freedom'. Harry was overjoyed. He couldn't believe that his baby's name was in the headline of a newspaper. He called his family back in Jalandhar on his landline and read out the headline and the article excitedly. He cut out the article and put it in a file. 'We will show it to her when she grows up. We will tell her that her parents taught her the value of freedom from an early age.'

A few months later, a letter arrived at home followed by a phone call. Harry was being transferred to Kashmir. He left soon after.

22

Gurmehar, Age Two
Jalandhar, 1999

I hear the *thuk-thuk* of his bike from far away. Mummy told me he was coming and that he wouldn't stay for long. He has to go to the Valley to protect us. I understand that but I'm just happy Papa is coming. Mummy told me that he needs to collect some things before he leaves. He is coming back from where he is posted to pick things up and say bye to me and my sibling who will be here soon. We have been living with Nani for the last few months because Dadi's house is being painted and the dust and smell of the paint irritate Mummy. We have a dog here too, a tiny white Pomeranian whom Nani loves to bits. She treats the dog and me just the same. Her name is Dixie. I love petting her and running around in the veranda with her.

They have opened the gate. The iron gate makes the loudest sound when opened but it is the sound of his military boots that make me jump down from my bed. I run to him as fast as I can. He is there waiting for me with his arms open. He is wearing his cargo jacket that has a million pockets. I put my hand in one of the pockets and, like I guessed, it has a chocolate in it. I look around and find the second pocket. This one has toffees, more than I can fit in my hand. The third pocket has chewing gum and the other two have a Frooti each. I hug him super tight, thanking him for all the gifts. He kisses my cheek and the stubble scratches me.

'I don't like this beard. It is itchy,' I say, running my hand over his face. I have a chocolate in one hand and the other hand I use as support, wrapped around his neck, my head resting on his shoulder. He is my favourite person. When I'm with Papa, I feel like there is no one who can harm me.

Mummy comes out and meets Papa. Her eyes are moist but she is happy. We know that Papa has to go back today. Mummy and Nani have prepared me for it. I cry every time he leaves. I cry every time anyone leaves. I love it when there are guests and people at home whom I love and the more I love them the more it hurts when they leave.

Papa is packing his bags and taking all the things he needs. He asks me if he can take my singing doll. It's the doll I love the most. If I kiss the doll's cheek, it starts singing. I laugh because the sight is so funny. And yet, here he is, my papa in his camouflage, holding my doll and asking if he can take it.

'Why do you want to take my doll, Papa? You don't play with dolls,' I say, giggling.

'This doll is like you, sweet and tiny, and since I can't take you with me, I'll take her,' he says.

'Where are you going?'

'To the Valley.'

'What is the Valley?'

'The Valley is a state which people call heaven.'

'You are going to heaven?'

'A place like that.'

'You can take my doll but you have to promise to get me two new ones.' I have played it well. I will get two dolls today.

'You ask me for anything and I will get it for you. Let's go and get all the toys you want.'

He wears his sling baby carrier and puts me in it. I love the baby carrier, it is the most comfortable thing to travel in. He tells Mummy that we are going to get toys for me and we will be back soon. He wears his cargo jacket over the carrier and zips it up so that I don't feel cold. He also drives the bike very slowly as I rest my head on his chest. We get to the shop and I pick up lots of small toys. He buys me everything.

It's time for him to go. I don't want him to go, so I start crying. I yell and hold his leg so he doesn't move. Mummy tries to loosen my hold but it doesn't work. 'Don't go,' I scream between sobs. My nose runs and my eyes hurt.

He doesn't know what to do. 'Okay, you want to come with me?' he asks me finally.

'Yes!' I say. Victory was close.

'Okay, go run to your room and wear your pretty sandals. But first give me a hug,' he says.

I give him a hug and run fast to look for my sandals. They are under the bed. I bend on my knees and pull them out. I slip my feet into them. I don't know how to buckle it, so I leave it. I try to run fast but the open buckles slow me down. I finally return to where I left him, but now he isn't there. He has gone. My mother picks me up and asks me not to cry. She consoles me, saying that he will come back, that he has just gone to the shop.

'Let's go take out your toys and wait till he comes back,' she says.

I believe her and keep waiting for him.

23

Jalandhar, 1999

Gulgul's little sister was born on 18 March 1999, in spring. This was Raji's favourite month because of her love for flowers and gardening. In their old house, she had maintained the most beautiful garden and there was always an undeclared competition between all the wives of the officers.

For the whole of last year nothing had seemed to make Raji happy. How could she be happy? Her husband was out on the front fighting, while she was waiting at home counting every second till he came back, if he came back at all, a thought she kept pushing to the back of her mind. She has lived in fear since the day he left. He called her as often as he could and they wrote to each other constantly but the calls were so difficult to connect and sometimes the letters didn't reach for months. She tried to get in touch with his seniors and unit members to ask about his whereabouts but they were not allowed to disclose the details. Those months when she didn't get any replies, she spent hours thinking of the worst things possible. She would stare at news channels all day, wondering if this would be how she would find out. She would hear about encounter after encounter; there was no second of calm. Her heart finally almost got used to the new speed it was beating at. Once, when Harry called, she heard bombing in the distance. She asked him about it.

'This is how it is here. It's far, in distance, not close to me. Don't worry,' he would try to reassure her. His voice was different. He was different. He did not have time for reassuring her and she knew it. This was what happened there; she was supposed to know this by now. The echoes of those bombs haunted her.

'Please stay safe, please call more. I keep watching the TV to know if something has happened,' she said. 'Something' was the code for death. They never used the word, it was always 'something'.

Harry laughed and went quiet. 'If something happened, they will call you first. You will know before the media.' It was a fact and she knew it. Why waste time watching TV and being anxious? He knew 'something' could happen, there was a real possibility. He was not someone who would zip himself up in a tent and let his men fight and die for him. One of his friends got injured and went back home to recover. He wrote in a letter that he would rather have died in the war than come back from it alive. Raji understood well what he meant. An officer could not live with that, live a normal life after seeing what one saw there.

Every time the phone rang her stomach fell. Was this the call?

It was a relief when it wasn't. She would take a deep breath and relax for that one second. This was not the moment, but the fear never left her. It could be any moment.

A call did come. It wasn't that call.

He had applied for leave around the birth of his second baby, just as he had for the first one.

❧

She was in the village when she felt it. She woke up in the morning with some discomfort and, by afternoon, it was not something she could have simply ignored. They called the midwife and left for the military hospital with her mother and daughter.

The word 'daughter' kept ringing in her head over and over again, the memories of the past flashing in front of her eyes. She knew what it was like to be born in a family with two girls—it was never easy. Growing up, she had often wondered, would things have been different if they had had a brother? Would people have been kinder, would their own family have treated them differently? Harry was in the city that day. He was at the hospital waiting for her.

March was the most beautiful month of the year. The weather was as perfect as it could get and the world glowed in the warm sun. She saw

Harry waiting for her in the parking lot, standing next to the car they had recently bought. Harry was not a car person. His heart belonged to his bike; the sound of the Royal Enfield was music to his ears. In the beginning, they had been more than happy with the bike, the wind in their hair, the small sense of freedom. Young love. It all changed when the little one came and the news of the other little one pushed them to get a car. A Royal Enfield, as beautiful as it was, could not accommodate their family of four, especially when the kids grew up. However, the Enfield never left its place. Every Sunday, Harry, Gulgul and their dog, Rustom, would go to the garage. Gulgul and Rustom, sitting next to each other, would watch as Harry washed the bike till it reflected like a mirror. The bubbles and foam were enough to entertain them both.

Gulgul saw her dad and ran at full speed towards him. Her tiny legs were still unaccustomed to running, but that did not stop her. There was Papa to hold her before she fell.

'What if it is a girl?' Raji asked, looking at him, unsure if it was a question she could ask. She knew how she felt, never wishing her own life upon a pair of girls.

'Then I will be the proud father of two incredible girls,' Harry replied, looking at her. He knew what she meant, he knew what a hard life she and Pammi had had. 'Do not worry, whether it is a girl or a boy, we will love the babies. We will raise them like champions and they will never have to struggle. I will make sure they get every opportunity to succeed. I promised you bangles with diamonds studded on them. When you come out with my little gift, they will be waiting for you. It doesn't matter if it's a girl or a boy. It will be my child, a piece of me, and if I know something about the baby's father and mother, I know this kid will be tough enough to take on anything in the world.'

∽

'It is a girl,' they were saying, a group of people sitting on the sofa next to her bed, talking to each other excitedly.

A girl.

She got up from her bed slowly, trying not lose her balance. He was waiting for her in the room, with Gulgul on his lap. She couldn't have been more excited.

'I have a sister!' she exclaimed, her eyes shining at the prospect of another child in the house, another child she could play with.

Unlike their first child, the newborn was in a crib that was in the room. A healthy, happy child. She realized she wouldn't have to wait to hold her like she had to before. Gulgul climbed up on to the bed and sat next to her, curiously looking at her mother as she held the baby in her hand.

She was the most beautiful baby they had ever seen, her lips translucent and cheeks pink with colour. The baby opened her eyes. Big almond-shaped eyes stared back at Raji. Her tiny body made herself at home in her mother's arms. Raji could not help but admire her innocent eyes and long eyelashes. She lifted the baby closer to her chest and got down from her bed. It was time to go home.

The military hospital looked especially beautiful on 18 March 1999. It was as if the spring was welcoming a flower-like child. It was the first time Raji had felt happy in a very long time. With her daughter in her arms and Harry by her side, walking in the beautiful military hospital garden, it seemed like life would be good from here. She knew she only had to convince Harry to take the Long Gunnery Staff Course (LGSC) exams instead of going back. Now that there was a baby, she felt sure he would stay.

ᔕ

He came home for three days. The war in Kargil was still going on, causing many deaths. There was a death in the family too and Raji needed him to be there for support. Three days was not a long time but it was enough—at least he was here. Harry came back with a fractured collarbone that he had not reported.

'Why did you not report the injury?' Raji asked, infuriated. Reporting it would mean he would be given rest. It would mean he would get to come back home and prepare for his exam. The war would pass them by and he would not have to go back. When he cleared his exam, he would be posted somewhere else. Raji spent hours preparing notes for him and reading from his books. She knew about military strategies and ammunition almost as well as he did. There were neatly made copies and spiral-bound photocopies ready for him. It was just one exam.

'If I tell them they will put me on rest for four to five months,' he replied matter-of-factly, as if coming back home was a bad thing. He had come back home a different man. It wasn't the Harry they were used to seeing. He was lost in his thoughts, watching the news with his fists clenched by his sides. Even those three days were too long for him.

Home felt strange. He opened the tap and there was water; he turned on the switch and there was light; he walked four steps and there was food. He cried the first night he was home. He stayed up the whole night watching his daughter sleep.

'I see Gul everywhere in Kashmir, in every child. The children are scared of us, so I keep toffees in my pockets to give to them. I take their pictures to remember their faces. We also play cricket sometimes with the kids of the village. They all look like her to me,' he murmured out of nowhere.

'Why don't you sleep?' Raji suggested.

'I don't have much time with you both and the third one. I want to look at you for as long as I can. Sleeping would waste this precious time.'

He did fall asleep eventually and when he did he talked in his sleep. He gave commands. He was still dreaming of the war.

'Why are you not studying for your exam?' Raji lashed out. He had not touched his notes.

'I'm not giving the exam. I'm going back,' he said as calmly as he could. There was no argument.

'No, you can't.' Raji broke down. Not after all this time. Not again.

'My men are fighting there. Do you know what kind of families they come from? Many of them are the only earning members of their families. They have small children, they have wives as young as sixteen, some have parents on their deathbeds. These men are out there fighting, risking their lives, and you want me to stay here in this magic castle where you open the tap and there is water to feed an entire village?'

'But you cannot go.'

'I have to go. I cannot live knowing I chose not to go.'

These were his final words on the subject. He left soon after that, to fight for the nation, to fight alongside his men.

24

Gurmehar, Age Two
Jalandhar, July 1999

He has come back home. He was gone for so long. Mummy used to be scared every day. Everyone at home was so upset. Every evening, we would sit in the living room with the TV on. I could see my mother trying to swallow air because breathing had become difficult.

This one time, I woke up in the middle of the night because I felt like throwing up and my stomach was hurting. When I woke up crying, I noticed Mummy was already up. She saw me and got up from the chair she was sitting on. The moment I started crying, she came running to me to check my fever. I told her how my stomach was hurting and I was feeling sick. She started crying. I had never seen her break down like that. She kept murmuring, 'How will I do this alone with two daughters?' over and over again.

Today she is happy. I can see her face glow. There is peace to her movements now. Her soul is at ease. She resembles her previous self. I want to go and sit on her lap.

Papa is back but he has a bandage on his neck. I ask him to lift me on his shoulder. It was our post-dinner routine. We would have dinner and at night he would take me out for a walk till the ice cream stand. Most of the time, Manu Chachu and Anu Chacha would also accompany us.

He tells me he cannot lift me up because he has injured his neck. I ask him to show me where it hurt. With my little fingers I poke at the edges of his bandage to see what the wound was like under the dressing.

'What happened to your neck?'

'A bad person and I were fighting and he pushed the butt of his rifle here,' he says, pointing to the injury.

'Mummy was saying something like this would happen all the time,' I reply, still trying to peel the dressing off, my curiosity getting the better of me. He doesn't flinch, he lets me poke.

'She also knows it is my job, my *farz*.'

'I know, she tells me that when I cry. I want orange ice cream.'

He takes my hand and we walk towards the shop.

∽

Mummy dresses me up in a little frock today and wraps the baby in a new blanket. The baby is like a toy. Mummy tells me she is my sister. We all go to the park—Mummy, Papa, my sister and I. This is a huge park with swings and a milk bar. I go to play on the swings and in one far corner I find a cage that has soft teddy bear–like animals. I run to Papa.

'Papa, what is this?' I ask, jumping. I want one for myself. A live teddy bear!

'That is a bunny rabbit,' he says

'Bani rabbit?' I ask. That is so strange. The new baby is called Bani too.

'Yes, they eat carrots all the time,' he says, pointing to the carrots in a corner near a water dispenser.

'Baby's name is also Bani! I want one. I want to take Bani rabbit home,' I say.

'We can't take her. We already have a bunny rabbit at home—your sister. You can play with her. She will be with you all your life; these rabbits run away.'

'Who knows? Just like you leave, what if she also leaves?' I ask.

'I will come back and then all of us will live happily. You, me, Mummy and Bani rabbit,' he says, picking me up.

'Promise me?'

'Promise.'

We walk towards Mummy. I want to go and see my baby sister. I have new-found respect for her. She will be there forever and I will never get bored.

'Mummy, I want to say hello to Bani rabbit,' I say as I jump up to sneak a peek at the little baby on her lap. She is smaller than a toy and her face is pink.

Papa comes and sits next to us. He gets us ice cream: butterscotch for her and an orange stick for me. The baby's nose starts bubbling with snot and we all laugh. Mummy cleans her up and she looks neat and clean all over again.

This is my picture-perfect happy family and I want it to stay this way.

25

Jalandhar, 1999

I woke up with a jolt at 1 a.m. I don't know what it was. My body had felt a current pass through; I think it was the damp wall that I had touched in my sleep. Gulgul and Bani also woke up at the same time and started crying. It was raining heavily. I have loved rains all my life but that day it scared me. I don't know what happened but I started crying with them. I kept asking them to stop crying but my own tears wouldn't stop. I was frightened out of my wits and all sorts of bad thoughts came to my mind. Eventually the three of us fell asleep.

The phone rang early in the morning. Anu, my brother-in-law, was sitting with me in the living room and we were having tea. I picked up the receiver.

'Hello?'

'Who are you?' a man on the phone asked.

'I'm Rajvinder, Capt. Mandeep's wife.'

'Can we have Capt. Mandeep's father on the phone, please?' he said.

'Oh, he is in the shower. What happened? You can tell me.' I panicked. Was Harry hurt? Was he okay? Why do they want to talk to my father-in-law?

'Is there anybody else?' he asked.

'My brother-in-law is here.'

Anu heard the panic in my voice and walked over, trying to ask me what was going on.

'Is he younger or older?' the voice asked.

'Younger.'

'We want to speak to Capt. Mandeep's father,' they persisted.

By then, Anu had gone to call his father, who came running to the phone.

'Yes, he is here,' I said and passed the phone to my father-in-law, my hands shaking.

His face dropped. The floor beneath my feet vanished. My father-in-law turned to me with moist eyes. The phone was in his hands and someone was still speaking on the line. By the time he put the phone down, there were two officers in full uniform at the gate.

He was no more.

I did not understand a word beyond it. One day, I had everything and the next day, everything was gone. My home had fallen apart, all my dreams, everything had been shattered in one blow.

When I couldn't move, they told me his last words to the solider who held him were, 'Take care of my Gulgul and Bani.'

He kept fighting, they said. He told the man next to him to wait. 'You only have a wife at home, I have two brothers too. I will go check the hill.' He took a bullet straight in his heart. The reports said it was his left ventricle.

We had built this house, this little family. I had bought curtains to put up in the new house. I'd had my heart set on a particular set of plates I had seen in the market. I knew we would buy them before his transfer. Our happiness were in the small things: in a plate, a new mug, curtains. We had built this life together with these little things.

We were supposed to be together for many, many more years. I had plans in my head. I knew what school our children would go to. I knew how we would raise them. He would be the loving parent and I, the strict one.

He used to tell me, 'When Gulgul grows up, I will drop her to college every day in my jeep. I would still be as handsome as ever, still very fit, with salt and pepper hair, and any boy who even looks at her will be at the receiving end of my deathly stare and flexed muscles.' I used to laugh at these silly things. He would say, 'Arre, why not? My daughters will grow up to be the smartest, most beautiful women in the whole world. Who will not want to look at them in awe?' He loved us. In one second, everything had been shattered.

The walls started closing in on me and my brain gave up. I couldn't think, I did not understand words, I couldn't form sentences. I was choking on air. I hated everything around me. I hated people, sounds, voices, trees, flowers, the sky. I hated the world and everything that was a part of it. How could everything around be so normal? How could the TV work like nothing had happened? I hated it. My body was numb,

I couldn't feel anything, my insides were numb. Everything made me sad.

I looked at my kids. Then it hit me—they only had me left. I would have to live. I did not want to live for even a second. Yet, I would have to because he asked me to take care of them, for him.

He was my world—I was so devoted to him. We had loved each other since we were kids. We had built our lives with each other and had grown up together. Harry would tell me about bikes and movies and I would listen to everything he said and watch all the movies. I never wanted too much from the world. I was happy with him and whatever little we had. He would go to work and I would look after the house, mend the gardens and try new recipes. This was our life, this was how we were supposed to be. My three-month-old Bani was yet to say her first words to him. He was supposed to be there when she took her first steps. Gulgul was soon starting school and he was to have driven her there. How was it possible that he was gone, just like that? How would I live without him? How would I do all these things alone? There were so many years to life—one day would pass and then the next, but what about the rest of the days?

His body came to the morgue on the second evening. I was so scared. What would Harry be like? How many injuries would he have had? I went in. I saw his feet first. I touched them, held them in both my hands and wept. I bent down and kissed them. I moved towards his face. I kissed his forehead and ran my hands through his hair. I knew it was the last time I could run my hands through his hair, it was the last time I could touch his face. There would be no tomorrow. He would be gone; this day was all I had. His face had a bit of powder on it and I wiped it off with my hands. He was smiling. I looked at his face and cried and smiled and then cried again. I did not want to leave. I wanted to be there with him for every second till he had to go—every second counted. I went to touch his hands. I wanted to feel the grip of his hand around mine, just one more time. But I couldn't find it. His hands were tied to him with a rope. I picked the cloth up and took them in my hands. For the first time, his hands were cold. He was the warmest, most loving person in the world. In freezing winters, he would sit on the bed and tell me he was warming it up for me. He would then move to the colder side of the bed and sleep while I sat on the warmer one. All his warmth had left him; that day he was cold.

Raje, do this. Raje, come here. Raje, do that. Raje, see this. Raje, Raje, Raje.

Who would call me Raje any more? Who would take my name like that? He was gone.

'Raje, take care of Gulgul and Bani.' His voice echoed in my ear. I would take care of them, I promised, but there were so many promises we had made. I had never thought this would happen to me. I had thought God would be kind to us, especially to us, that he would not do this to my family again, but he did. I lost faith in Him then.

We came back home and he came with us. He loved giving me surprises since the time we were in college. After we got engaged, he would come home suddenly with mithais or samosas for me. Even after he went to the Valley, he would come home unexpectedly and surprise me. Once he was in Delhi and we had a fight. I was on the phone fighting with him till 2 a.m. and went to bed crying. I woke up the next morning to the bell ringing at 5.30 a.m. I saw his shoes from the gap in the bottom of the gate. His friends were training to fly choppers, he said, and he had asked his senior if he could get on to the first chopper to

Adampur, a few kilometres away from Jalandhar. He had come to say sorry and give me a surprise.

I was not prepared for this shock.

Before leaving, he had said to me, 'I'm giving you a date—17 August. Pack all your things. I will be getting my next posting when I'm back. If you don't have all your things then, I will leave you.' He would always make me laugh. I spent all this time sending out clothes to dry-cleaners and packing the curtains I had bought. I had saved up enough for the plates and I was going to buy it on 16 August. His aviators were wiped clean and stored safely in a trunk, his clothes ironed and all his perfumes bubble-wrapped. I had taken care of everything. The boxes were marked and they were already piling up.

On 6 August 1999, he attained martyrdom.

Epilogue

When I was sixteen, right after my class X exams, we went to Srinagar for Papa's unit's raising day. We've always been invited for the celebrations the unit held. As children, we used to love attending this function. As a family, we were never very socially active and over the years, I've understood why. Awkward silences, abrupt halts, carefully skirting topics of conversation. I never wanted to be friends with children around me and Mummy never quite had the time to socialize. This was the only party we would attend the whole year. The army culture is such that children are never allowed for the actual party but in the officers' mess, there is always a room called the children's room, full of games and toys. It was like a dream, a party in itself. The mess in Papa's unit in Ludhiana—a city only a few kilometres from Jalandhar—had a badminton court where I remember spending hours playing.

In the evening, lavish food would be served in the children's room while we sat and went through the DVDs kept for us to watch. For us, it was never about the party but about getting to live a single day of the life we could've had. It was the day that answered a question I've asked myself, my mom and my God a million times: 'What if he were here?'

As the sun came up after a whole night of celebrations, and we drove back to Jalandhar with Mom behind the wheels—away from the life we could have had—our reality would hit us. The little girl in me found solace in Cinderella's story. Year after year, like Cinderella, we would run away. Cinderella found her happy ending. Would we ever find ours?

It was the first time we were visiting Srinagar but I had been here before in my dreams. I had thought about these lands, the hills, the texture of the soil, the chill in the wind for years, wondering what it must have felt like to him, wondering what was the last thing he saw before he went away forever. Did his eyes see a dark sky shimmering with blinking stars or did he see glimpses of the sky through the heavy canopy of chinar leaves? I was only sixteen, yet I could feel the conflict like a chill in my bones. Coming back to the unit felt like coming back home to an extended family, to a place where you know you are loved. But the love I received was a reminder of everything life could have been, should have been, but will never be.

All my life I have wanted to be like my father, but as I grew up and understood life and emotions, I realized that while I wanted to be an image of my father I also wanted to grow up to be the woman my mother was. The day after the raising day function in Srinagar, we went to Chak Natnus in Kupwara, the village where his company was posted the night the encounter happened. The village was a two-and-a-half-hour-long car ride away from the capital. All my life, growing up, I had imagined the place where he passed away to be a barren ground with cracks in the earth, the soil red with all the bloodshed, but it was far from what I had imagined. The sun shone. The clouds were slowly marking their presence in the sky. A slight drizzle came like a blessing. This was exactly how I had imagined *jannat* to be.

The commanding officer of the area at that time was a kind human being, a dashing officer. My father would have been just like him had he been here.

Even today, I keep trying to picture Papa. I try to age his boyish features, but I never quite get it right. I wonder what he would look like right now. Would he have the salt and pepper hair he always wanted or would he have kept a beard, would he have gained weight with age or would he have remained the bodybuilder he was in his college days? One day, time will get to me and I will surpass the age of thirty and probably have wrinkles on my face and the wisdom of the years, but the memories of my father will remain the same: ageless, immortal.

We left for the village along with a civilian who was there the night it happened. I didn't know what that meant at that time but in the army *jonga* I sat right across from him, looking at his face for answers to the questions I had had all my life.

'Do you remember what he looked like?' I asked, my eyes big and bright, looking for a piece of him to complete my puzzle, to complete the image, to create the memories I didn't have.

'Uh, yes, he spoke Punjabi, sported a beard and wore his hair short,' he said. His eyes were unable to meet mine, his gaze wavering, his answer short.

'No, tell me more,' I urged. This wasn't enough. But by now I could imagine Papa the way he was when he fought, with no shaving kits or hair salons available in the depths of the forests he lived in while he served; with no luxury, away from home, in the range of the enemy, on a constant vigil, his heart burning with love for his people and his nation.

'Gul, later,' my mother said, glaring at me. I did not understand what had happened until much later. I had shared a car ride with a man who was on the other side, a man who might have been responsible for what had happened to my father.

Something shifted within me, something that I will never be able to put a finger on.

I had written Dad a letter the previous night in the mess. I left it there for him, buried in the soil.

ᔕ

Dear Papa,

I'm sixteen years old now. Every day since you left, I've thought about you. How you were, where you would be, what you might be doing. Death is my favourite subject to read about. Oh, and I read. English is my favourite subject in school but I really, really do not like maths. I know you loved it. I tried liking it, I even took private tuitions, but it is not something I can really enjoy. I'm sorry. When I was in class III, our English teacher asked us to read any Enid Blyton book as holiday homework. I remember thinking it would eat into my time of playing out in the sun, but little did I know that in doing so, I would find something that I would use as my fortress in life. I read the first book and fell in love. It was the first time in my life that I had fallen in love with something, something that wasn't you or Mummy. One day I want to write a book. I want to tell our story. Each and every story that I have read or heard or watched, I've carried a piece of it inside me and I've used it to build myself. I know I am human but today I'm also a collection of a million thoughts and ideas that make me feel infinite. I want to share my life with more people. Maybe if they feel how I feel, I would have someone who 'knows'. I'm hoping maybe then I won't feel so alone.

Bani and I are also national-level athletes. Mummy has put us in a boarding school where we train day in and day out to be the best tennis players in the country. I dream of representing India. The tricolour, the three colours dominating my last memory of you, acts as my driving force. Bani is one of the best players in the country. She wins almost every tournament she plays in and is being trained by the best coaches in the country because they really believe in her. She is incredibly brave. I wish you could see her play. She is fearless, just like you, never holding back from hitting the ball as hard as she can. My coaches think I'm extremely hard-working. I don't know if I'm hardworking or not but when I'm on the field or on the court and things get tough—a close match or high temperature—I think about you and how you kept fighting and survived the worst conditions. I keep reminding myself I'm more than just a chubby girl with a tennis racket; I'm a warrior's daughter and I keep pushing myself to be that.

I just took my class X exams. We are doing the British curriculum because Mummy feels it will give us more exposure. I am sure you already know this. In my heart I know you've been keeping an eye on us, helping us in tough times, but I'll tell you one thing about Mummy: she has done everything for us. She is an officer too, just not in the army. She doesn't take nonsense from anyone. I have learnt that from her. She is tough like a rock. I want to be like her when I grow up. On her own, she has built us a home and a family, a tiny one but a family nonetheless. We have a beautiful house with lots of flowers. The walls are different shades of pinks, pastels and whites with your pictures everywhere. We never feel you are not there; your presence is always in the air, as if you are just round the corner, waiting for us to come and say hello. Every room has photos of you and our living room has your painting. In the house, there is a wall meant for you and it is of a different colour. The decorations are bullet shells, the awards you received and the emblems of your units. Every Sunday, Mummy sits in the veranda with a bowl full of Brasso and cleans them till they reflect like a mirror. She has been doing it for years.

This year, we adopted a dog, a white Pekingese, and named him Ace. Ever since he came home, Mummy hasn't stopped talking about Rustom and how you and he were like brothers. She keeps recounting the incident when you lost Rustom and the entire unit went out in search of him. She tells me your heart was big enough to accommodate everyone equally. I really want to convince her to get another dog and name it Deuce.

I often wonder what life would've been like had you been here. We go to tennis tournaments alone, Bani and I, because Mummy has to go to office. Our opponents come with their coaches and their whole families. They come with little umbrellas and ice boxes and sit near the fence to watch their children compete against us. They are always there to cheer their children on. Our opponents always have a face to look at when they are feeling angry or sad or when they make a mistake. I have Bani to look at and she has me. Sometimes, the draws are such that we are competing with each other and those days are the worst. I think tennis has toughened us up. We have learnt how to block out the noise and how to survive alone. We learnt it a little too early but we learnt it well.

We really miss you. I wish you could see me play tennis. Sometimes I believe that you do. Sometimes

I hear your voice when I'm down in an important match. I keep believing it's you, cheering me on. We all really miss you and are very proud of you. I hope one day we can make you proud too.

We love you and miss you. I love you and really, really miss you. It's futile but I will still say it. My heart still hopes and believes in miracles. Come back, Papa, and I promise I will give away every comfort in the world to look at your face again, to hear your voice again, to have your hand on my head, to have you say my name again. If you come, I'll introduce you to Bani and I will introduce her to you. I will tell her that between the two of us I'm your favourite but she won't mind. In that moment she will just be happy to finally meet you.

I will have to say goodbye for now. We will meet you again in another jannat, a jannat where humanity and happiness are still alive.

Love,
Gulgul

Acknowledgements

To all the people in my family who have shared their personal histories and memories with me so that I could write this book. To the women in my family, Dadi Ma, Nani Ma, Maasi, Mummy and Bani, for teaching me how to be strong and to all the men in my family, Dada Ji, Masar Ji, Manu Chachu and Anu Chachu, for never doubting that strength.

To Pinky Ma'am, my class IV English teacher, for being patient, loving and kind to a very lost nine-year-old. With your guidance I found my love for reading books and a dream for writing one.

To my teachers in Lady Shri Ram College (LSR), New Delhi, Rita Joshi, Madhu Grover, Rukshana Shroff, Arti Minocha, Maya Joshi, Shernaz Cama, Mitali Mishra, Arunima Ray, Dipti Nath, Maitreyee Mandal, Janet Lalawmpuii, Ngangom Maheshkanta Singh, Karuna Rajeev, Wafa Hamid, Jonathan Varghese, Taniya Sachdeva and Rachita Mittal, for teaching me, loving me, dealing with my random interruptions in your class and more than anything for standing up for me and letting me know that LSR will always be my home—a safe haven where I can be free in every sense of the word.

To Urvi, Navya and Ishrat for being my home away from home.

To Chandrika, Vallavi, Kanupriya, Sidika, Mehak and Deep for being my anchors and 'proxy' givers—without you my life would not have been complete.

Students everywhere who care about the state of the nation, thank you for standing with me and thank you for keeping the fight going. To idealist brains who think they can change the world, you really can!

To Manasi Subramaniam for finding me and being there for me at every step of the journey, with this book and beyond.